Petticoat Doctors
The First Forty Years of Women in Medicine at Dalhousie University

Enid Johnson MacLeod
With an Introduction by Barbara Hinds

Pottersfield Press
Lawrencetown Beach
Nova Scotia, Canada

Acknowledgements

I thank all those who provided material for these 46 biographies, and especially Dr. Judith Fingard, Dr. Rosemary Gill and Dr. Irene Szuler. I also thank Carlotta Hacker for providing many valuable references, and Barbara Hinds for countless hours of editing.

Copyright 1990 Enid Johnson MacLeod

Canadian Cataloguing in Publication Data

MacLeod, Enid Johnson, 1901 -

Petticoat Doctors

ISBN 0-919001-60-2

1. Women medical students -- Nova Scotia -- Halifax -- Biography. 2. Women physicians --Nova Scotia -- Biography. 3. Medical Education -- Nova Scotia -- Halifax -- History. 4. Dalhousie University. Faculty of Medicine --History. I. Title

R692.M32 1990   610.69'52'082   C90-097573-3

Pottersfield Press gratefully acknowledges the assistance provided by Barbara Blauvelt at the Dalhousie Medical Alumni Association office who helped to make this book possible.

Support for this publication was provided to Pottersfield Press by The Canada Council and The Nova Scotia Department of Tourism and Culture.

Pottersfield Press
RR 2, Porters Lake
Nova Scotia   BOJ 2SO

Women Graduates in Medicine 1894-1933

1894	Annie Isabella Hamilton	
1895	Katherine Joanna MacKay	m. MacKenzie
1896	Clara Mary Olding	m. Hebb
1897	Martha Wyman Brown	m. Shaw
1898	-	
1899	Mary Leila Randall	m. Morris
1900	Winnifred Brenda Braine	m. Reynolds
	Victoria Ernst	
1901	Florence Maud O'Donnell	m. Piers
1902	Martha Agnes Philp	m. Bradshaw
1903	Minna May Austen	
	Grace Elizabeth Bernard Rice	
1904	Eliza Margaret MacKenzie	
	Jemima MacKenzie	
	Stella May Messenger	m. Pearson
	Blanche Margaret Munro	m. Crawford
1905	Mary MacKenzie	m. Smith
1906	Annie Hennigar	m. Sanford
1907	-	
1908	-	
1909	-	
1910	Bessie Angela Bober	m. Houston
	Minnie Grace Spencer	
1911	Eliza Perley Brison	
	Euphemia Bessie Balcom	m. Davis
1912	-	
1913	-	
1914	Jean Augusta Maclean	m. Hunter
1915	Elizabeth Kilpatrick	
1916	Louise Alberta Pennington	m. Collier
1917	-	
1918	-	
1919	Florence Jessie Murray	
1920	Annie Almira Anderson	nee Gilchrist; m. Dickson
	Ella Pearl Hopgood	
1921	Mabel Gladys Patterson	
	Mildred Resnick	m. Glube
1922	Grace Theresa Mary Cragg	m. Vasaturo
	Anna St. Clair Creighton	m. Laing
	Christena Catherine MacLeod	m. MacLauchlan
	Elizabeth Hope Thurrott	

1923	Margaret Rebecca Chase	m. Collins
	Phebe Kirsten Christianson	m. Thompson
1924	Lalia Barclay Chase	
	Alice Evelyn Thorne	m. Wade; m. Morrison
1925	Roberta Bond	m. Nichols
	Anna Margaret Murray	m. Klebart
1926	-	
1927	Marion Robertson Irving	m. O'Brien
	Eva Waddell Mader	m. Macdonald
	Evelyn Frances Hyslop Rogers	
1928	Charlotte Munn	m. O'Neil
1929	Irene Viola Allen	m. Macpherson
	Anna Isabel Murray	m. Dike; m. Musgrave
	Marie Jean Whittier	
1930	-	
1931	-	
1932	-	
1933	-	

Introduction

In 1988, Dr. T. J. Murray, Dean of Medicine, Dalhousie University, appointed a "Women in Medicine" committee to plan the celebration in 1990 of the enrolment of the first woman in medicine at Dalhousie. By 1989, 566 women had graduated in medicine from Dalhousie. This is the story of the forty-six women who graduated during the first forty years—from 1894 to 1933.

Since I was a young girl, I have been interested in women in medicine, and since becoming a medical doctor, I have been active in the Federation of Medical Women of Canada. When I was asked by the dean's committee to write about the early women graduates, I looked over the list and found that from 1930 to 1933 no women graduated in medicine. This may have been an effect of the Depression, although no other medical schools in Canada showed a reduction in women during those years.

These forty-six graduates present a variety of personalities, as well as many similarities. Many were missionaries and many were graduates of Pictou Academy, a high school famous for its classical education, which provided Canada with educators, doctors, ministers and premiers for many years. Some of our medical women were in business, and others left the country and were lost to the records and archives. It is regrettable that on some of these women there was not more information, but it is very impressive that most of them were outstanding in their careers at a time when there was little encouragement, and often much opposition.

Many of these women were personal friends of mine over the years and I was encouraged in my own career by their example. I know some of the problems they had, and I admire them for their fortitude and determination. It must have been much more difficult in Victorian times when women were expected to stay at home or choose careers such as teaching, nursing and secretarial work.

My own career, in the thirties, was remarkable for its coincidences. I enjoyed medical school, due mainly to a class of very understanding and kind men who were exceptionally considerate and helpful, but I did not find it easy to get a residency following graduation. However, when I did get one, it was with Dr. Griffith, at the very time he was doing research with curare as a muscle relaxant during anaesthesia, and I was fortunate to be a part of this. Later, when we moved to Dartmouth where there was no hospital and no bridge across the harbour to Halifax where the hospitals were, I had to give up anaesthesia. Within a short time, I was offered a position in the Department of Physiology and Biophysics at Dalhousie Medical School, where I finally became assistant professor and made a whole new career for myself.

Many of the women in this book would have had experiences like mine. Most of them, as I, would have had encouragement from family and friends and fellow students to help them through the difficult road to their career. I hope you will enjoy these brief biographies.

Enid Johnson MacLeod

Pioneer Women Doctors:
The First Forty Years of Women in Medicine at Dalhousie University

Historically, medicine was practised by men only. Yet in the Victorian era, with its social climate of male dominance, prejudice and obsessive modesty, a few women dared to seek entry into this exclusive male domain.

In Canada in the mid-1800s, a few tenacious young women began to canvass and badger universities for admission to medical school. These pioneers usually had enlightened parents and a persistence now called feminism. They found Canada's university doors were closed to them. Obstacles were either created or shored up by a threatened male hierarchy. If a woman wished to study medicine, she had to go abroad.

The first woman to graduate in medicine on this continent was Elizabeth Blackwell. She obtained her MD in 1849, at Geneva Medical College, New York State, and went on to found the Women's College of the New York Infirmary, where Canadian women were able to study medicine. Several other U.S. medical colleges began accepting women while Canada continued to drift behind in the surge towards equality.

Prior to 1879, no Ontario medical school would accept women as medical students, and any Canadian woman who had obtained her degree in a U.S. medical school found, on her return home, that she was denied the right to practise.

The Council of the College of Physicians and Surgeons of Ontario would not recognize a woman's qualifications and continued refusing to license women physicians until about 1880.

In Nova Scotia, it was not until 1881 that Dalhousie University passed a regulation allowing women to be admitted to study medicine.

Another thirteen years passed before the first woman graduated in medicine at Dalhousie. She was Annie Isabella Hamilton, "a fiery, determined little individual," who became a missionary in China.

She was one of the few Victorian women in Canada who dared to shake the pillars of social propriety. By doing so, she and her fellow pioneers paved a way for the growing ranks of women doctors. Today, their successors find it difficult to imagine the opposition these dauntless women had to overcome.

The prejudice Victorian women fought is illustrated in an editorial published in a Kingston newspaper:

> We should be sorry indeed to know that Canadian maidens or matrons either were so dead to that modesty which is woman's chief charm, as to sit unmoved side by side with young men, and listen to lectures on obstetrics or anatomy.... To think of disclosing the human form divine, over which humanity bids us throw a veil of decency, or of having the most sacred of feminine mysteries freely discussed before a mixed class of young men and young women is not only shocking, but disgusting and degrading.

Notwithstanding the opposition and the unorthodoxy, Victorian women pressed through the doors of universities to be trained in medicine.

In the years between 1894 and 1933, a total of forty-six women graduated in medicine from Dalhousie University. Their brief histories have been compiled to mark the enrolment of courageous Annie Hamilton in 1888 as Dalhousie's first woman medical student, more than one hundred years ago.

Barbara Hinds

Annie Isabella Hamilton.

In the late summer of 1888, a farmer's daughter made social history in Nova Scotia. Annie Isabella Hamilton, aged twenty-two, entered Dalhousie Medical College. She was registered as the first woman student to be admitted for the study of medicine. (About twenty years previously Dalhousie had accepted its first women students to non-degree programs in science and the arts).

By all accounts, Annie Isabella Hamilton spent a very active four years at Dalhousie. She was not only a good student, but she also found time to develop her interest in the Chinese language and culture. Among her classmates, she was well known for her views on the need to emancipate the social status of women and for her campaign against the use of alcohol and tobacco.

She was born on March 17, 1866, in the township of Brookfield, Colchester County, Nova Scotia. On both sides of the family, her ancestors were robustly individualistic men and women who belonged to a prosperous farming community which traced its roots to the first settlers of Brookfield.

Her paternal grandfather was known as a man of learning and possessed a significant library, which may have sparked the many ideas which took shape in the mind of young Annie Hamilton. Her father was known as "Queer Bill," which, in those days, was an unabashed reference to the fact that William Hamilton was an individualist—he marched to his own drum.

Curiosity and a sense of adventure were apparently strong traits in all of William and Mary Hamilton's children. Annie's brother, Henry, left for Utah at an early age and combined a prosperous career as a self-taught electrical engineer with an abiding interest in poetry. A collection of his works was published posthumously. A second brother also moved to the United States and pursued a career as an engineer. A third brother wandered far and near for many years, before returning to Brookfield to die. Annie's only sister, Florence, emigrated to Idaho Falls, where she married an American and together they operated a florist shop.

While not a great deal is known about Annie Isabella in her very early years, undoubtedly, she, like the other family members, possessed a very independent spirit, which clearly manifested itself in her later life.

She was raised with strong religious beliefs in an age when the life of a missionary abroad had considerable romantic appeal. At the age of fourteen, she distinguished herself as a Collector for the Home and Foreign Missionary Society of Brookfield by raising $12.63, one third of the total raised in 1880. She had started on her lifelong commitment to the disadvantaged and poor.

It is known she was somewhat of a misfit. She spent little time cultivating her feminine appearance, and shortly after school opened, the boys sent a paper around the class to get her one of the affairs the other girls wore—"a bustle."

One classmate described her as being "very plainly dressed, rather colorless, with straight, thin hair, and not very attractive." Yet the girl who went with her to Pictou Academy in two different sessions and later to Dalhousie, wrote fifty years later: "I knew her very well and loved her, all her good points were not outward, they were in her head and heart. The night before her graduation, a girl who boarded in the same house put her (Annie's) hair in curl papers and she appeared on the platform with curls all over her head. To me, it was no improvement, Annie needed no curls."

History shows that the men in her class were no more successful in persuading her to wear more feminine attire than she had been

in her attempts to win them over to her strong temperance and feminist views.

Records of the time indicate that Annie Hamilton graduated from the Normal School, Truro, in 1882, and the Pictou Academy in 1884, where she received a gold medal. One can only surmise at the forces which propelled the young Annie Hamilton into an academic career when the more likely course would have been a life as farm wife and mother. But neither she nor her siblings stayed down on the farm.

Annie was only seventeen years old when she became a school teacher, and when she was barely twenty, her mother and father died within two weeks of each other. Still, she hoped to dedicate her life to being a doctor, and with savings from her salary and help from her brothers living abroad, she knew she could pay her tuition fees. Nevertheless, it appears that she took a two-year break in her studies, 1890 to 1892, probably to earn money for her fees.

She sought enroled at Dalhousie in 1888. Faced with a young woman of high intelligence and burning commitment, the medical school authorities reached an unprecedented decision and agreed to accept Annie—the first woman allowed to enter the male medical preserve in Nova Scotia.

Little is known about her life as the only woman in a class of fifteen at medical school, except that she failed in her efforts to have smoking prohibited in the operating theatres.

In 1894, she graduated from Dalhousie College as a Doctor of Medicine and Master of Surgery, the first woman graduate in medicine in Nova Scotia, and her compassion for the sick and poor soon found expression. She set up a practice in the working-class district of Halifax's North End, where few other doctors had ventured, and she spent almost nine years there. She was well known and popular in the various neighbourhoods, although she was regarded as an eccentric by those who chronicled events of the day. She made her house calls on a bicycle.

In 1903, Annie Hamilton became associated with the Presbyterian Mission of the United States, and after spending some time learning the Chinese language, she, like several of her contemporaries, went to China to work as a teacher and medical missionary. She spent the rest of her life in China, returning to North America only once, in 1936.

Little is known about Dr. Annie Hamilton's work and life in China between 1903 and 1920, but from the accounts of her colleagues in China, she worked under very difficult social conditions with limited medical resources, administering to the ailments of the poor, and the abused women and children in her district.

After 1920, her health began to deteriorate from her many years of hard work. She had various ailments, including arthritis, and as a result, she devoted much of her time to teaching and writing. She wrote a number of textbooks in this period, one was on English language for her students at the university. She was apparently a regular contributor to the *Montreal Witness,* a publication of the Presbyterian Mission.

A letter, written in 1931 to her brother, Bennie, shows she wished to visit Nova Scotia. She wrote, "I am saving up my pennies now in the hope of visiting my kith and kin." But in the same letter she referred to her financial woes and wrote, "There has been such a slump in silver that a Chinese dollar now is worth less than 25 Canadian cents. So, you see, I cannot afford to pay my proper debts." (She still owed her brother $100 and it lay on her conscience.)

In letters to her cousin Carrie, she chronicled the social upheavals of Bolshevism in China and the war in Manchuria, and revealed her impoverished state and a singular preoccupation with economizing. She wrote, "I bought these embroidered goods in Mokanshan and was going to mail them from there, where I was next door to the post office; but on account of the zonal system for parcels, I should have paid more, so I brought them down with me to Shanghai."

In another letter, written in the same period, she wrote:

This is the third year that I am teaching in the preparatory department of the Sun Yat Sen University, one of the important universities of China. Although I was engaged to teach in the preparatory department, I was loaned to the science department and the agricultural department for a year and a half to teach English.

There, I was teaching in the Shanghai YMCA High School when you last heard from me. Since then I taught in a municipal council school in Shanghai and afterwards was a science teacher in the Shanghai High School which is the largest high school in Shanghai. It was also under good discipline but when the Bolshevists got the upper hand of the students, formerly well behaved students were turned into fiends. So I left that school after four and a half years.

In 1936, she travelled to the United States to see her brothers and to meet church officials, but, probably because she could not afford to do so, she did not visit her "kith and kin" in Brookfield.

Dr. Annie Hamilton was seventy-five years old when she died in Shanghai on December 21, 1941. In her final years, she continued to correspond with her cousin Carrie, in Brookfield, but she showed no inclination to return to Canada.

To the end of her life, she was passionate about her missionary work. She remained outspoken about her beliefs and the need to help the disadvantaged. She brought a religious zeal to all aspects of her life, but, according to her nephew Leonard Hamilton, who later told the story to Ada Spidle (the daughter of Carrie Hamilton), she always considered herself to be at home with the Chinese people. Her enduring interest in her mission is hard to understand in today's liberal, non-secular age and, no doubt, her assumptions about the backwardness of the Chinese society would be questioned.

She believed that the Chinese were "her people" and that they would always need her. Her lifelong dedication to improving living conditions and to the alleviation of suffering amongst the Chinese transcended ideological values. This was her enduring legacy to the people of China.

Her legacy in Canada was an opened door of opportunity. A century ago, she had been the lone vanguard who crossed the threshold of Dalhousie Medical College—an exclusive male preserve. Against great odds, with courage and determination, she led the cavalcade of women who cared to follow her; and today, women never question their right to the opportunity of a career like Annie Hamilton's—in medicine.

Katharine Joanne Mackay

was the second woman to be granted an MDCM from Dalhousie Medical College, and she was also a Pictou Academy graduate. Kate was one of ten children of whom one sister was a nurse, one brother was a doctor and another an educator. Both brothers were anxious for Kate to study medicine and offered to try to get her into McGill University, where no woman had ever been admitted to medical school.

Meanwhile Kate went to Boston and graduated from the School of Nursing established by an associate of Dr. Elizabeth Blackwell.

Kate's certificate was signed by seven women doctors. Inspired again, Kate came back home and attended Dalhousie and obtained her MDCM in 1895.

For a while, she practised medicine in New Glasgow, with her physician brother, and then she went to work in a government post in Honolulu, Hawaii, when the voyage was long and perilous round Cape Horn.

She sailed back to Canada and went home to Plainfield, Pictou County, in 1902, and she married a former neighbour, John R. MacKenzie. Shortly thereafter, they moved to Edmonton where Kate practised medicine for a few years before they moved to B.C., finally settling in Port Coquitlam where her husband became the mayor, and she continued in general practice until she retired in 1918. She died in 1925 of septicemia. She was known as "one of the most highly respected public citizens in Port Coquitlam."

Clara Mary Olding

graduated in 1896 and received a handwritten notice from the registrar of the Provincial Medical Board with a transfer certificate, permitting her to practise in New Brunswick.

She went to Saint John, New Brunswick, and opened an office in a house on Charlotte Street, where she lived with two sisters. She adopted her own style of dress, always wearing a white uniform, and became a distinctive figure as she made her way on foot, in all weathers, through city streets to make home visits to the sick.

Her personality not only endeared her to her patients, who were mainly women and children, but her demeanour and competence also helped to overcome a widespread prejudice against women doctors, and in time, she became secretary of the almost all-male Saint John Medical Society.

At Dalhousie she had met a medical student by the name of Andrew Hebb, who graduated in 1902, six years after her own graduation. A long correspondence ensued between them while she was practising in Saint John. Some of these letters are still avail-

Clara Olding in the Anatomy Laboratory.

able, and Hebb, in addition to expressing his love for Clara, said he did not wish to interfere with her practice of medicine. In the course of time Clara accepted Andrew Hebb's proposal and in 1903, they married, and she went to Chester to join Hebb in his medical practice.

At this time Hebb was in partnership with Dr. G.R. Morse and they had a large rural practice in the countryside surrounding Chester. Morse later moved away, which meant that much of the time Hebb was out of town, visiting patients in distant communities and farmsteads.

Clara took care of his local patients at this period, plus most of the maternity work. Meanwhile, they had four children: Donald (1904), Andrew (1905), Peter (1909), and Catherine (1911).

An interesting anecdote is told of the Hebbs and a man called Hennigar who was a devout Liberal (Hebb was a Tory). Hennigar ran a slaughterhouse in the town of Chester. Hebb, as medical officer of Chester, made him move it outside the town. A hatred was built on these facts and Hennigar refused to let any of his family go to Dr. Hebb, but he welcomed Clara when they needed medical attention.

Clara was one of ten children in a Pictou County family of Scottish and English stock, and she was very proud of her heritage.

In Chester she was very active in community affairs and was on the committee for the erection of a war memorial.

Chester is not an area of Scottish settlers, and some of her grandchildren are inclined to think the kilted highlander on the war memorial in Chester is due to Clara's influence.

For eighteen years the Hebbs continued a practice in Chester and then moved to Dartmouth. Less than two years later, Clara died of bowel cancer, on June 18, 1921.

Her obituary read

> At the time Dr. Olding-Hebb completed her medical course, public opinion was not what it now is as regards the professions for women, and it required altogether exceptional initiative and independence of character for the young girl to enter what was then considered to a very large extent the exclusive preserve of the man. However, the quality of her personality and her essential womanliness won the day and wherever she practised she established herself securely in the confidence and regard of the community.

In 1922, her husband, Dr. Andrew Hebb, established a fund for a memorial prize to be called the Dr. Clara Olding Prize. It is awarded annually to the Dalhousie Medical School graduate with "the highest aggregate in examinations of the fourth year; character and previous scholarship being taken into consideration."

The memorial prize is acknowledged by a letter signed by the president, Dr. Stanley MacKenzie.

Dalhousie University
Halifax, N.S.
Office of the President,   October 4, 1922.

Dr. A. M. Hebb,
166 Portland Street,
Dartmouth.

Dear Dr. Hebb:
I wish to acknowledge the receipt of your letter of the 3rd. inst. expressing a wish to establish an annual prize in the Medical faculty by the name of "The Dr. Clara Olding Prize," as a memorial to your late wife. I wish to express my fervent appreciation of your desire to associate this memorial with the Medical School of the University, and would like to be allowed to say that I cannot think of a more beautiful way to pay a tribute to your partner in life, for she was a partner in every sense of the word. It is also most appropriate on

account of the fact, that, as you state, she was one of our earliest women graduates, and particularly one of those women who have proved to the world their full right to exercise the profession of medicine by the success she had in it.

I shall bring the matter before the Faculty and Senate of the University at the first opportunity. I know they will all be as appreciative as I am and I shall send you formal word of their action. In the meantime may I thank you in my own name and in theirs for associating the University with your tribute to Mrs. Hebb.

Sincerely yours,
Stanley MacKenzie.
President.

Martha Wyman Brown

was born in Yarmouth in 1874,   and graduated from Dalhousie Medical School in 1897. She married Dr. Howard Shaw and together they studied in Vienna, Austria, and in London, England. They went to Ashland, Oregon, where they had "a large and lucrative practice," and Martha practised until her death on April 6, 1948. She had one son, Marvin.

Mary Leila Randall

graduated from Dalhousie in 1899. Born on January 13, 1868, she was a daughter of Edward George and Elizabeth Randall and was baptized on February 26, 1868, as Mary Eliza Campbell Randall in St. Mary's Anglican Church, Bayfield, Antigonish County, Nova Scotia.

After she received her MDCM at Dalhousie, she took graduate studies and went to Sydney and practised as a paediatrician for at least five years. She married an engineer, Frederick Cox Morris, who worked at the Sydney steel plant. They invested in real estate and owned at least one apartment building known as the Randall Apartments. Just three years after she married, she developed Bright's disease and died at the age of forty-four on January 19, 1912, and she is buried at Bayfield.

Winnifred Brenda Braine

and her brother, Dr. W.B. Braine, were natives of Grand Pré, and classmates, aged 21 and 20 years, when they graduated from Dalhousie in 1900. The following year, Winnifred married another classmate, Dr William P. Reynolds, and she went with him to Bute, Montana, where they practised medicine together.

When she died October 5, 1942, she was health officer for the town of Stephenville. So deeply was she respected that the business offices closed for two hours on the day of her funeral.

Victoria Sarah Ernst,

a graduate in 1900, was born in 1856 at Bridgewater and began her professional life as a teacher, living frugally and saving up to pay her way through medical school. Twice she gave her savings to her father because he was burned out and lost his possessions.

At the age of forty she had again resolutely saved enough to enter college to train as a doctor. She was a small intense woman who had "big eyes like an owl," and long after she graduated, her professors remembered her for her questions and eagerness to learn. Her classmates used to say "Victoria, by the Grace of God, Miss Ernst."

Miss Ernst led her final year, but because she was a woman, she was not allowed to intern. When she demanded her rights, she was told, "Very well, but you'll have to sleep with the other interns."

On graduation day in 1900, as she went up to get her degree, her classmates rose in a body and sang, "God save our Gracious Queen."

Dr. Ernst developed a practice in Bridgewater and its environs and worked there for thirty years. She never married, but she loved children and had great compassion for orphans and adopted several boys. In one case at least, she asked for the most unwanted boy in the orphanage and gave him a home.

Always dressed in black, her long skirts and loose cape-like coat became well known in the town. She was "thrifty," the townsfolk said, after her father was seen poking among the ruins after a fire levelled half the buildings on Main Street. He was looking for nails to straighten for the maintenance of his daughter's properties and other undertakings.

When she died on October 4, 1940, at the age of eighty-four, she was a woman of property, with forty houses, and the local paper said she paid more taxes than anyone else in town. In her will, some of her houses were left to her tenants.

Florence Maud O'Donnell

was born in Halifax, Nova Scotia, on August 4, 1877. Her father, John O'Donnell, was born in Ireland in 1840. He was an orphan of the potato famine, and like thousands of Irish children of that time was transported by ship from Cork to North America, arriving in Halifax in 1855 at the age of fifteen. Her mother was Mary Ann Laurilliard, a direct descendant of John Christophor Laurilliard who, with Cornwallis, came to Halifax at its founding in 1749 and was buried in St Paul's graveyard.

Miss O'Donnell entered Dalhousie in 1894, and graduated as a Doctor of Medicine, Master of Surgery, in 1901.

After a year as an intern in a Halifax hospital, she went to Chengtu in Szechwan province in central China to be medical doctor in the hospital training school and orphanage which were supported by the Women's Missionary Society of the Canadian Methodist Church.

After arriving by ocean liner in Shanghai, getting to Chengtu was an astonishing adventure. Small steamers could navigate the Yangtze River to Nanking, Hankow, and as far as Ichang. At this point passengers transferred to houseboats which had to be towed

British Consular Officers with Chinese authorities in Chengtu, 1907.

Dr. Florence O'Donnell in front of Chengtu Hosptial, 1907

by 75 "trackers" on the river bank. They pulled all the way upriver with long ropes, always against the current and against rushing torrents in the gorges.

It took travellers two months to reach Chungking, and a further two months to get to Loshan, at which point the Ming River made for easier passage northwards to Chengtu. The last two weeks of this incredible journey were made by sedan chair, sleeping at inns where they were available, and under the watch of hired armed guards for protection against bandits.

The whole trip from Shanghai to Chengtu took over six months, and could be done only in winter in the low-water period.

Chengtu is the capital of Szechwan province, mainly the centre of farming. Once there, Dr. O'Donnell took charge of the women's hospital, which she later had enlarged, and she also organized a training school. Her colleagues in Chengtu were the staff members of the university which was built at that time by Canadian, French, German and English joint efforts, all under the auspices of the Methodist Church.

Very few details are known of young Dr. O'Donnell's day-to-day life in Chengtu, but an excerpt of her report to the Methodist Conference of 1907 reads as follows:

> To the hospital comes the little slave girl, sometimes almost murdered by ill-treatment and neglect; the childless wife begging to be helped as her husband is about to discard her; the 13-year-old daughter-in-law whose mother-in-law has beaten her eye out; the weak and puny child whose poor little inflamed and suppurating feet testify to the cruel practice of foot binding; the thin emaciated wreck in the bondage of opium; and in the midst of it all the call comes to go out at once to an opium suicide.

After six years in China, Dr. O'Donnell took the long and hazardous trip back to Canada and to Halifax to get married. She had been in Montreal on her way to China when she met her fiancé, William Harrington Piers of Halifax.

He had followed her to Toronto and proposed marriage to her instead of many years of duty in China, but to no avail. Young Dr. O'Donnell was committed to go as a medical missionary to the hospital in Chengtu.

After seven long years of patient waiting, she and Mr. Piers were wed in October 1908. Like her own maternal great, great, great

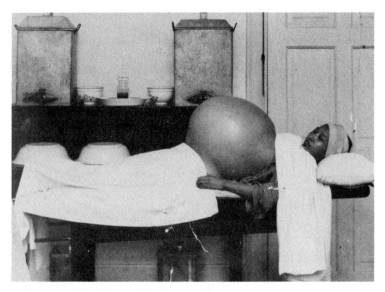
A patient of Dr. O'Donnell in Chengtu Hospital.

grandfather, Mr. Piers's forebear, Lewis Piers, was also one of the founding fathers of Halifax with Cornwallis.

Following her marriage, she ceased to practise medicine and dropped her medical appellation. She and her husband took up residence on Pryor Street in Halifax, and enjoyed a summer residence in Chester from 1916 on.

They were members of St. Matthew's Church, and she was an active member of the Princess Louise Chapter of the Imperial Order Daughters of the Empire. During both world wars, Mr. and Mrs. Piers were generously hospitable to members of the armed forces.

Dr. Florence Maud O'Donnell Piers died on September 28, 1958, twenty years after the death of her husband, aged 81, and is buried in the family plot in Camp Hill Cemetery. They were survived by three children, Walter McLarren Piers of Halifax, Rear Admiral Desmond William Piers of Chester, and Emily Virginia Finch-Noyes of Victoria, B.C.

Although no records of her six years in China are known to exist, all three of her children inherited many Chinese artifacts of considerable value. One such legacy was an attractive scroll of Chinese characters which Commodore Piers hung in the library of the

Commandant's House at the Royal Military College in Kingston, Ontario.

One evening when members of the new Canada Council were being entertained, the Dean of Oriental Studies from the University of Toronto asked if the scroll pertained to a family member. When informed that no one knew the significance of the scroll, the learned professor then translated. It was a most laudatory tribute from a high-ranking mandarin lady "to the wonderful white lady who came from far away across the oceans to heal all our illnesses. She saved the life of our daughter, and when asked what reward would she accept, the lady doctor humbly requested that our daughter's foot should be unbound and never be bound again." The ornamental cloven foot shoes removed from the feet of this child for a reward, as requested by Dr. O'Donnell, are still proudly held in the family's possession.

Martha Agnes Philp

graduated in 1902. She was the daughter of the Rev. R.R. Philp, Halifax, and, like so many zealous young women-doctors of her day, she became a medical missionary and journeyed to Chengtu, West China, under the auspices of the Women's Missionary Society of the Methodist Church. She travelled in the company of Dr Mabel Cassidy Mortimer, who had graduated the same year from the University of Trinity College.

Martha married Dr Frederick Joseph Bradshaw, a fellow missionary, and together they spent many years of service in China. When they retired, they went to live in Burbank, California.

Minna May Austen

was born in Halifax and was one of two women in the class of 1903. This class at Dalhousie took the first examination of the Provincial Medical Board, and Minna May Austen was the first physician registered by the board.

In 1907 she was appointed by the Women's Missionary Society of the Methodist Church to West China as a medical missionary. At this period in Canada's history, about one quarter of all women medical graduates became missionaries.

After studying language in Chengtu for a year, she was appointed to Women's Hospital in Kiating, and in 1909 she went to Women's Hospital in Chengtu.

In 1917 she became seriously ill and was compelled to give up her work. She returned, frail and ailing, to her home in Halifax, but when the call went out for anyone with medical training to help relieve the suffering of the thousands of people injured in the disastrous Halifax Explosion of December 6, 1917, she joined the Halifax Dispensary staff and worked exceedingly hard in makeshift hospital tents and damaged hospital buildings during that bitter winter.

This devotion to duty, following her breakdown in China, so injured her health that for some time Dr. Austen was more or less an invalid. She died at her home, 352 Robie Street, Halifax, at the age of forty-five, on May 24, 1923 and was survived by her mother.

Grace Rice

was a native of Weymouth, Nova Scotia, and following her graduation in 1903, she was a resident physician in the Massachusetts
State Hospital for six years. She then went overseas and took
post-graduate courses in obstetrics and gynaecology in Dublin and
in Edinburgh, returning to Canada in 1911.

She had her home and her office in a red brick house on Spring
Garden Road, near Brunswick Street, and her sister, Frances, who
had served as an army nurse in World War I, looked after the
household and kept Dr. Rice's accounts. The house still stands
(1989). She was in practice there for almost fifty years and retired
in 1951.

A kind, gentle person with a soft pleasant voice, she was greatly
beloved by her many patients as well as by the medical students
who sought her advice. She quietly performed many acts of charity;
not only did she provide medical care without payment to many
people, but she also gave money to poor patients when she saw
need.

One of her protégés, Mrs. Audrey Buchanan Murray, a retired
public health nurse now of Grimsby, Ontario, recalls the encourage-

ment and financial help she received from Dr. Rice over many years.

She writes that she was caring for one of the doctor's patients in return for her board, so she could attend high school in Halifax, when she first met Dr. Rice, and the doctor seemed to take her on as a daughter. Dr. Rice "carried her" through high school and provided Audrey with enough money over many years to pay for tuition and uniforms while training as a nurse at Halifax Infirmary, and later, when she took a course in public health nursing at the University of Toronto. "Dr. Rice was a great lady. Only she knew how many young people she helped with their education."

Dr. Rice died at her home in Halifax in 1963.

Blanche Margaret Munro

was one of four women in the graduation class of 1904 at Dalhousie Medical School. She was the daughter of a clergyman, and after graduation she became a missionary in India. On her return from furlough, she married the Rev. J. A. Crawford, who was living at River John. He was originally from Scotland and had been studying at Dalhousie University when Dr. Munro was a student. After their marriage, she did not return to India, although she remained interested in missionary work. She gave up the practice of medicine and moved to Edinburgh with her husband.

They had two children, and during World War I she entertained Indian troops at her home in Edinburgh and is said to have surprised and pleased them by speaking to them in their own tongue. In her later years, she moved to Aberystwyth, Wales.

Jemima MacKenzie

was born August 18, 1872 at Waterside, Pictou County, youngest of the twelve children of Simon and Ann (Murray) MacKenzie. She was the second of the four women graduates in the class of 1904 to become a missionary.

While still studying in grade eleven at Waterside, she also taught school, and went on to teach at Pictou, Scotch Hill and Saltsprings. From the latter, she walked the twelve miles home, every weekend, in order to assist her ailing mother in household chores. She was twenty-six years old when she completed grade twelve at Pictou Academy, but she had never lost sight of her goal, and by teaching she earned enough money to study medicine at Dalhousie Medical School in Halifax.

Jemima had been only a child living on a subsistence farm when she had made her decision to become a medical missionary in distant India. Her older sister Mary (Mollie) shared Jemima's ambition for a missionary's life, and she too studied medicine at Dalhousie.

When Jemima graduated in 1904, she led her class in surgery. A few weeks later, in July, her mother died. The day after the funeral, she left for Boston to earn the $200 needed to pay the cost of her sister Mollie's final year at Dalhousie. That autumn, Jemima was appointed by the Women's Union Missionary Society of America, New York, to medical work in Cawnpore on the River Ganges, in India.

On arrival, she took charge of an orphanage and girls school with 170 pupils. At the request of American missions and British administrators, she went to the Allehabad-Fatephur district near the Ganges river, a densely populated place without a hospital or treatment facility of any kind. During the first month she lived in a tent. She learned the language and soon rented a house for a hospital.

Dr. MacKenzie travelled on foot and horseback. She rode elephants and camels, and drove in a bumpy two-wheel cart on rough roads to visit patients in the countryside. Often she was threatened by bandits and frightened by wild animals. On one occasion she had to take the reins from a hysterical driver and drive her cart through the lonely jungle where panthers could be seen from the track. Twice she shot deadly snakes with a revolver she carried.

She had a preventive and curative practice for all emergencies, whether apprehended or real—it was the power of prayer. When danger loomed, she knelt and humbly placed her fate in God's hands.

In 1907, at Fatephur, she took over a dispensary, established with the aid of money given by Americans. Every day she managed clinics, and every day, every patient was given Bible teaching. The institution at Fatephur which was Dr. MacKenzie's place of work for many years continues in service.

With British aid, a sixty-bed hospital was opened. Six dispensing buildings were rented in villages, and one of them, thirty-five miles distant, was named for her mother, Ann Murray. Outpatient duties took her fifty miles from the main base, and it was not until 1926 that she had an automobile.

When her hospital opened in 1911, a training school for nurses was established with it, and to this Dr. MacKenzie gave her talent. Except for the nursing staff, which she had trained in the early years, she had no experienced help. She cared yearly for 600 inpatients, and some 20,000 dispensary outpatients.

After risking her life in checking the spread of an outbreak of Asiatic cholera in 1919, she was decorated on the order of King George V, with India's highest award for public service, the medal Kaiser-I-Hind.

Dr. MacKenzie returned home to Pictou in 1921 on a well-earned furlough, during which she cared for her aged father and found time to direct a mission school in the family home at Three Brooks. In 1923, Dr. MacKenzie was back in India, working under the auspices of the Canadian Presbyterian Church, in charge of several hospitals, one of which was also a leprosarium.

It was a common practice for Indian mothers to abandon babies, especially girls, on the banks of India's sacred River Ganges, and in her years in India, Dr. MacKenzie adopted forty-four abandoned children, ten of them legally. She had them educated, and started them on careers as useful members of society. Three of her boys did mission work. Many of her girls became nurses.

When she retired in 1939 and returned to Canada, she brought two of her adopted sons, aged four and six years, to live with her in Pictou. In 1940 Dalhousie awarded her an honorary doctorate in laws and the Canadian Medical Association made her an honorary member.

She engaged occasionally in medical practice until the infirmities of age prevented her working any longer. She was eighty-four years old when she died on January 27, 1957.

A fitting tribute to her memory took place on August 2, 1981. A Dayspring Communion Service was held in Pictou at which her biography was read by one of her adopted daughters from India, Sarina MacKenzie Bayer, and the sermon was preached by Rev. Bruce Munro, her grand-nephew. The offering taken was sent to the Neemuch Children's Home in India, a home for 250 abandoned children, in memory of a great lady, the daughter of a farmer, a teacher, missionary, surgeon, physician, surrogate mother of forty-four orphans—Dr. Jemima MacKenzie.

Eliza Margaret MacKenzie

of the class of 1904 was not related to her classmate Dr. Jemima MacKenzie. It is recorded that she was born at Flat River, Prince Edward Island, the daughter of Mr. D. MacKenzie.

She was described as "tall and stunning" in appearance, and, after her graduation, she set up as a general practitioner in Prince Edward Island. Intelligent, but perhaps too beautiful, she apparently found it difficult to cope with and adjust to the competition and the prevailing attitudes towards women doctors in Charlottetown.

She left after a short while and went to New York where she trained in St. Luke's Hospital as a nurse and little more is known about her career. Dr. Eliza MacKenzie practised as a nurse until she died in about 1930.

Stella Messenger

was born in Bridgetown in 1879 and was the fourth young woman to graduate in the class of 1904. She practised for a short time at Lunenburg and then went to England for post-graduate work. There she met and married Phillip Pearson, a civil servant. She returned to Canada with her husband, and during World War I, she covered a country practice of a twenty-mile radius around Sherbrooke, Guysborough County.

Later she went to Lawrencetown, in the Annapolis Valley, and practised for ten years. While there she encountered personal tragedy when her only child, a daughter, a first-year medical student at McGill, was killed in a coasting accident. Shortly afterwards, Dr. Messenger-Pearson left the area and moved to Yarmouth, where she immersed herself in a busy general practice.

The *Nova Scotia Bulletin* stated that she made many friends and came to be held in high esteem by all who knew her. She died in Yarmouth on December 29, 1932.

Mary MacKenzie

was the only woman in the graduating class of 1905. She was
known as "Dr. Molly," and was a sister of Jemima, who had
graduated the previous year.

Mary was born September 12, 1867, at Waterside, Pictou County, and received her education in Waterside and at Pictou Academy.
After graduating from medical school, she served abroad as a
missionary and was appointed to Cawnpore, India, where she was
engaged in medical and bible work for five years.

She then took a post-graduate course in eye, ear, nose and throat
diseases in London, England, and in 1911, she returned to Canada.
The following year, she married the Rev. Alonzo A. Smith of New
Glasgow, Nova Scotia, and they went to Verchoyle, Ontario.

While Mr. Smith took a ministerial charge, Dr. Molly became
the first doctor to do medical inspections in rural and urban schools
in Ontario, working under the auspices of the Women's Institute.

Later, she worked as a medical inspector for the Department of
Education, Ontario, in Gravenhurst, Granton and Colborne. She
retired in 1935, at the age of 69.

In 1938, Dr. Molly started a world tour, leaving Halifax by ship, crossing the Atlantic Ocean to Great Britain, then through Europe to the Holy Land, India, China and Japan, returning in 1939 by ship across the Pacific Ocean to Vancouver B.C., then across Canada by train to Nova Scotia. She died after a brief illness on April 30, 1955, at her home in Pictou, at the age of 87. She and her husband are buried in Lorne Street Cemetery, New Glasgow.

Annie Norman Hennigar,

daughter of David and Martha Ann (Faulkner) Hennigar, was born in Noel, Hants County, July 9, 1873. She received her early education at the village school, where she later became a schoolteacher, before she entered medical school. She graduated with the class of 1906.

She practised in Burlington, Hants County, Nova Scotia, for a few years, then in the fairly isolated area of Cheverie, where she remained until 1919.

Her staunchness and colourful character were soon recognized. She was said not to be a society lady or fashion enthusiast. "If there was a fashion show in the village and someone told her that army worms were eating the grain in a farmer's fields, she would go to see the latter."

At Cheverie one night, after a heavy snowstorm, she was called out to a patient. Her sleigh upset in a drift and she was unable to get it back on its runners, so she looked around for help. She saw a light glimmering in a house some distance from the road, and she decided to go there. She was able to get her horse unhitched and clear of the sleigh, and with one rein she tied her bag of instruments across the horse's back. With the other, she led him across the fields as she reasoned they would not be drifted as badly as the lane. She had almost reached the house when her way was obstructed by a long board fence. She thought the boards looked old, so she heaved on them and broke them and got her horse through. The men in the house went with her back to the sleigh, lifted it back on its runners, hitched up the horse again and watched her as she continued on her way to her patient.

She said later, "Fortunately, I had great strength in the hands for a minute." And that was why she could extract fifty teeth in one morning, even after she had officially retired.

She was always known as "a grand man with a tooth," and one old gentleman, who as a child had been her patient, recalled, "When Dr. Annie hooked on a tooth and pulled, it had to come, even if your jaw came with it."

She was a real horse-and-buggy doctor, travelling in all weather, in all seasons, to deal with every type of illness and emergency. Many people in that rural area of Nova Scotia owed their lives to Doctor Annie. One such man she was called to operate on after his hand was mangled in a threshing machine. He was placed on her dining-room table, and with her hired girl holding the chloroform mask, and her husband holding the victim steady, she sewed the bone back in his arm and completed the usual procedures. There was no infection afterwards, and the man recovered, his arm fully healed.

In 1920, she returned to her native village of Noel, and for thirty more years she practised in Noel and Maitland.

Towards the end of her career, she wrote to Dr. Roberta Bond Nichols (Dalhousie 1925):

> My 'Horse and Buggy Days' were full to overflowing with hardships, thrills, dangers, determination and profit. In looking back, I would not have missed that period for a cool million.
>
> Amputations, fractures, dislocations, tonsillectomies, extraction of teeth, etc., all came my way and I was simply put on the spot as there was no one else to do it.
>
> I do a little oil painting and have been made a member of the American Physicians' Art Association. I want to paint a number of scenes that happened in my life denoting courage beyond what is normally expected of a doctor in performance of duty.

Dr. Annie described a picture she was painting at the time. It illustrated an incident which occurred when she went out on an urgent house call. It shows her safely leading her frightened, blindfolded horse past two bears on a lonely road. She had covered its head with the wagon lap robe to quieten its panic.

Some years ago, the Annapolis Valley journalist, Ken Miller, wrote of the event. Late one afternoon, Dr. Annie had been called out to deliver a baby. Her horse, Monty, was brought out of the stable and hitched up while she hustled about gathering things into her black bag. There was no time to be wasted and she settled down the horse to a steady jog trot.

Along a lonely stretch of country road, Monty suddenly came to a rearing stop, which almost dislodged Dr. Annie out of her seat. Monty's head was high and his muzzle pointed straight towards a clump of trees bordering the hillside road. She soon saw the source of trouble. Weaving down through the trees were two black bears, heading for the road.

Dr. Annie talked reassuringly and clucked to the horse, giving the reins a little tug. Unwillingly, Monty started off up the hill, but his step was high and halting. He was still frightened. He stopped and reared again.

Dr. Annie got out of the wagon. The horse's eyes were wide and rolling. Monty would not be reassured, so she backed him down the hill into a side path, threw a blanket over his head and held on to his bridle. After a while, the bears shambled away. Dr. Annie recovered her black bag which had spilled out of the wagon, led the blindfolded horse past the danger point and then they clopped on their way.

Years later, a man was looking at some of Dr. Annie's paintings. Among them was one of her faithful old horse, Monty. The man had stabled Monty many times, in all weathers, when he had brought Dr. Annie to attend his wife's confinements and their children's illnesses. He walked across the room when he saw the painting, folded his arms and gazed at it. In a reverent manner he said, "That's dear old Monty."

Dr. Annie had many interests. She was a great gardener. She hooked rugs and made beautiful quilts and loved birds and flowers. For her, there was beauty in everything.

She was interested in the young women who studied medicine, and her advice to the girl graduates of her day was, "Get out in the country where you are so urgently needed, especially if you are not afraid of work and enjoy an outdoor life."

Dr. Annie spent her life in rural Nova Scotia, and was married to Frank Northup Sanford of Noel on March 10, 1920. He had been her groom and stabled her horse. They had no children. She was in practice for forty-four years, remaining active until just before her death on August 9, 1950.

Minnie Grace Spencer

graduated in 1910 and became a medical missionary under the American Missionary Board in India. She worked devotedly there for about fifteen years in busy crowded hospitals, but her health failed and she had to retire. She returned home to Halifax, where she died around 1925.

Bessie Angela Bober

was twenty-one years old when she graduated in medicine in 1910 after having first earned a BA from Kings College, where her father was Professor of German.

After taking a post-graduate course in psychiatry in New York she became a psychiatrist and was on the staff of the Northampton State Hospital in Massachusetts for eighteen years. She was chief of the women's division and worked happily under the superintendent, Dr. John Houston, whom she later married. After his death she was consulting psychiatrist to the Dickensen Hospital and later did part-time work for the Veterans' Administration in the Veterans' Hospital in Springfield, Massachusetts.

There is a story about her which says she was pretty and vivacious as a student, and another story which says she carved her initials, "B.A.B.," not only among all the other initials on the old wooden benches, but on the cadavers as well.

Eliza Perley Brison,

a Dalhousie graduate of 1911, stands out among the great figures in the history of social welfare in Nova Scotia. She was a physician and psychiatrist, who did pioneer work with the mentally retarded in the province.

Dr. Brison was born November 15, 1881, in West Gore, Hants County. She spent her early life in this little village, and after completing high school she started a career in teaching. Her first job was in Rawdon Gold Mines, where she remained for one year. Following this, she spent a year teaching in Belnan, and two years in MacKay Section.

Dr. Brison then left the teaching profession to enter Dalhousie Medical School. A lack of funds prevented her from completing her medical course in consecutive years, so she took one year off and taught school again at MacKay Section to earn enough to enable her to return to Dalhousie.

She was fully justified in saying, as many others of that time could say, "I worked to get my education. The government did not give it to me." She successfully completed her medical course and graduated in 1911.

Dr. Brison's original intention in studying medicine had been to become a medical missionary, but a severe physical handicap prevented this. During her early twenties, she had a hip joint removed and she had to walk with crutches for the remainder of her life. That she did not allow this handicap to deter her in any way from her goal in life adds further credit to her illustrious career.

As an alternative to becoming a missionary, Dr. Brison specialized in psychiatry. Following graduation from Dalhousie Medical School, she went to the Northampton State Hospital, Massachusetts, for her residency in psychiatry. After one year there, she was forced to resign because her hip began to trouble her. She returned home to West Gore where she remained until 1918. During 1916 and 1917, in spite of ill health, Dr. Brison cared for mentally retarded children in her home.

By the summer of 1918, her health had improved to the point where she could resume her work and studies. She then registered as a student at the Walter E. Fernald State School for the Mentally Deficient. Her course there provided her with insight into methods of caring for and training retarded children.

Following the completion of her course, Dr. Brison returned to Nova Scotia on July 24, 1918, to become superintendent of the Imperial Order Daughters of the Empire (IODE) Home for Feeble Minded Girls in Halifax. Donations had poured in from IODE members across the country for the care of children affected by the Halifax explosion. The fund was generously oversubscribed and with the money left over, the IODE Home at 401 Quinpool Road was built for $16,700, and Dr. Brison had in her care ten to twelve mentally retarded girls.

Using to the full the training she had received in the United States, and her own personal qualities, Dr. Brison demonstrated for the first time in Nova Scotia that seriously retarded young people could be taught to work and to live useful lives if given proper guidance and specialized training.

After seven years of hard work by Dr. Brison, the institution was forced to close in 1925 due to lack of funds. Dr. Brison, however, never forgot the young women who had been in her care. She continued to visit them at the county homes where they were placed, and sent them gifts at Christmas, Easter and on their birthdays. Many of her acts of kindness went unnoticed by all except the recipients.

During the years 1925 to 1929, Dr. Brison experienced further prolonged periods of illness. However, these did not interfere with her work. In 1929 she became an anaesthetist at the Victoria General Hospital, Halifax. She was the first female doctor ever to be employed at that hospital.

Two years later she joined the staff of the Department of Public Health through which the provincial welfare program was administered, and she became a psychiatrist for the Province of Nova Scotia. It was not her first association with the department, for she had served as a consultant on a part-time basis while working at the IODE Home for Girls.

In her new capacity she travelled over the province testing children, counselling parents and helping welfare agencies. She did not drive a car, so she made her journeys by train, bus, sleigh and team, and she always kept her appointments, even if it meant working late into the night.

She carried a work load that would stagger a physically fit person, yet she refused to slow down. Even her summer holidays were not restful, as she spent many of them at clinics in Boston and other American cities in order to gain more knowledge about the behaviour of children and adults.

In 1931, she was given a life membership in the Nova Scotia Society for Mental Hygiene. That society, founded in 1908, is now the Canadian Mental Health Association, and Dr. Brison was one of the original members. In May 1952, the society presented her with an award for outstanding service and she was awarded the Coronation Medal of Queen Elizabeth II.

On April 20, 1963, Dr. Brison was made the first honorary life member of the Canadian Association for the Help of Retarded Children (later named the Canadian Association for Mentally Retarded).

Three years later, in recognition of her distinction and leadership in psychiatry, she was made an honorary life member of the Canadian Psychiatric Association. She also was made an honorary member of the Federation of Medical Women of Canada.

When Dr. Brison retired in August 1951, she was serving as consulting psychiatrist to the Nova Scotia Training School in addition to her duties as provincial psychiatrist. Her retirement was more theoretical than actual, for she continued to serve whenever needed.

On a number of occasions she was acting superintendent at the Interprovincial Home for Young Women at Coverdale, New Brunswick, and she also acted as superintendent at the Halifax Infants' Home when required.

In her later years, Dr. Brison lived with a niece at West Gore. She never lost her gentle, unassuming manner nor her sharp wit, and even when she was critically ill, she still demonstrated the fine qualities which contributed towards her great achievements and the awards she merited. She died on New Year's Day, 1974, aged ninety-two years.

Euphemia Bessie Balcom,

class of 1911, was born in Aylesford, the daughter of Dr. Parker Balcom, who at one time was president of the Nova Scotia Medical Society. She had a brother, Paul, who also was a doctor, practising in Berwick.

After graduating from Acadia Ladies' Seminary in 1907, she attended Dalhousie Medical School, graduating in 1911. She practised for a short time in Petite Riviere, Lunenburg County, and in 1919 she married Dr. Frank Davis and moved to Bridgewater.

She did general practice, mostly with women patients, and assisted her husband, giving the anaesthetic when he performed surgery. In the early 1930s, her husband was the mayor of Bridgewater, and he later went into politics and became minister of health for Nova Scotia. He suffered a fatal heart attack while attending a meeting of the Nova Scotia Medical Society at Ingonish in September 1948.

Following this, Bessie Davis, who was of a shy disposition and had been a great golf player, built a retirement home in Bridgewater. She later moved to a nursing home in Truro, where she died in 1967. They had a son, Paul, named after her brother.

Jean Augusta MacLean

graduated in 1914. She was born in 1889, the eldest daughter of Dr. and Mrs. J. W. MacLean, who gave her every encouragement when she said she wanted to become a doctor, like her father.

Following her graduation from Dalhousie Medical School, she went to Boston for two years to study psychiatry. In 1916, she went to Edinburgh to study in the medical school. In 1918, she received an MD from Edinburgh University, and was married to Joseph Hunter, a medical student. They had three children, Ruth, Frances and Joseph.

According to her daughter Ruth, Dr. Jean Hunter was an intellectual and she never became domesticated, employing a governess to look after her children. She was a strikingly beautiful woman, with bright red hair and green eyes and very musical. She sang in the St. Giles Cathedral choir in Edinburgh.

Her husband, Dr. Joseph Hunter, practised in Dumfries until 1927, when he was elected to Parliament. They moved to London, where he continued to practise medicine.

Jean also was interested in politics, and, at the time of his second nomination, Joseph had meningitis, so, leaving her husband in the care of two nurses, Jean went to Dumfriesshire to carry on his election campaign and make the speeches. She was successful. He was re-elected.

In 1935, Joseph died of a heart attack, and Jean, at the age of forty-six, returned to Edinburgh University and took up her studies again, receiving a diploma in public health. She went to work at the Crichton Royal Institute as a psychiatrist, remaining there until the outbreak of World War II in September 1939. She then returned to general practice in Dumfries, where she died of cancer in 1943.

Jean returned to Nova Scotia only once, when her father died, and she spent a short time in North Sydney helping to settle his estate. Her only son, Joseph, was killed in World War II at the age of twenty-four years. Her daughters live in Britain.

Elizabeth Kilpatrick,

born in Sydney Mines, February 27, 1892, graduated in medicine in 1915. and in 1925 she received an MD from Long Island College of Medicine in Brooklyn, New York. She was a pioneer in North American psychoanalysis.

Following twenty months of general internships in Women's Hospital, Detroit, Michigan, and the New England Hospital for Women and Children, Roxbury, Massachusetts, she took psychiatric residencies when the specialty was in its infancy.

The training was long. Dr. Kilpatrick spent the years from 1916 to 1918 at Northampton State Hospital; 1918 to 1920 as assistant physician in charge of women's wards at the Nova Scotia Hospital; 1920 to 1922 at Boston Psychopathic Hospital; and from 1922 to 1928 at New York Hospital, Westchester Division.

In addition, she was child psychiatrist at Vanderbilt Clinic, at New York Hospital outpatient department, and at Payne Whitney Clinic.

She was a graduate of the American Institute for Psychoanalysis, a diplomate of the American Board of Psychiatry and

Neurology, and lecturer in mental hygiene at Teachers' College, Columbia University from 1925 to 1932.

From 1932 she was on the faculty of the American Institute for Psychoanalysis, where she was a member of the faculty council, lecturer, training and supervising analyst, and from 1952 to 1954 she was dean.

Her sweet disposition and attractive personality made a great impact on people who met her and the American Journal of Psychoanalysis later wrote of her that when she left New York in 1959 she was

> not only our colleague and teacher, but also our dearest friend ... many felt that the very special place she occupied in our lives could never be filled... she was the 'good mother,' always present, always listening, always accepting....
>
> She was unfailingly kind and gracious in all of her professional and personal encounters.... She maintained a spirit of fresh delight in people, places and things.... There was a sense of abundance about her which made her company especially pleasurable.

Dr. Kilpatrick was a life member of the American Psychiatric Association, charter fellow of the Academy of Psychoanalysis and of the American Association of Existential Psychology and Psychiatry, honorary member of the Association for the Advancement of Psychoanalysis, and life member of Dalhousie Medical Alumni Association.

In 1960, she returned to Halifax and joined the Faculty of Medicine at Dalhousie University where she played an active part in teaching psychoanalysis and child psychiatry.

She retired July 1, 1968, and when she died on November 11 the following year, she bequeathed close to $500,000 to Dalhousie Medical School to assist the teaching program for medical students in outpatient departments and psychiatric clinics affiliated with Dalhousie, for the training of young psychiatrists, and for cancer research.

At the time of her death, Dr. R.O. Jones, head of psychiatry at Dalhousie University wrote:

> Dr. Kilpatrick demonstrated her ability to succeed in a man's world and to gain the respect and love of her colleagues of both sexes, and still maintain her femininity ... at the time when it was a pioneering step for a person of either sex she went on to specialize in psychiatry, and later, still an adventurous pioneer, she turned to

psychoanalysis and started personal analysis of the classical Freudian type.

But she became dissatisfied with what she seemed to be achieving, and in the early 1930s went to hear another famous psychiatrist—a woman—Dr. Karen Horney.

Dr. Horney, an earlier follower of Freud, had fled to America from Nazi persecution. She was one of the few in America who had the courage to find fault with 'the Master'... and ... became one of the founders of the so-called neo-Freudian school on this continent.

Dr. Kilpatrick was so impressed by the new insights which Dr. Horney presented that she started further study of personal analysis along Horneyian lines. She remained an important member of this group for the rest of her career.

(It had been on the death of Dr Horney that Dr Kilpatrick had become dean of the American Institute.)

On retirement Dr. Kilpatrick and her sister decided to make their home in Halifax and despite her being of an age at which most are content to give up professional responsibilities Dr. Kilpatrick immediately resumed hers.

She became a respected and much beloved friend to all members of the department; she brought new insights to our work, and new skills to the treatment of many difficult patients.... She became part of the 'family' in a very short time. Most important, she served as a refuge for many a puzzled, bewildered student. We profited much from her stimulation, her new and often different kind of knowledge, and even more her warm humanity. She certainly left her mark on the practice and profession of psychiatry.

Louise Alberta Pennington

graduated in 1916, and in 1917 she was appointed house surgeon to the Wolverhampton and Staffordshire General Hospital at Wolverhampton, England.

She married Mr. F. C. Collier and lived in Ottawa in the 1950s. They retired to Florida in the 1960s. She died in 1974.

Florence Jessie Murray

graduated in 1919 after a remarkable apprenticeship as a medical student in the catastrophic Halifax explosion of December 1917 and the epidemic of influenza, which followed the next year.

She became a gifted physician, an inspired missionary and devoted teacher. Her career was momentous and when she was awarded an honorary degree of laws at Dalhousie University in 1956, she was described in the citation as "one of the great women of the world."

She was born in February 1894 at Pictou Landing, a daughter of a divinity student who later became a Presbyterian minister, and she grew up in manses in Nova Scotia and Prince Edward Island. She knew she wanted to do something different with her life—not teaching, nursing or stenography, which were the limited expectations of educated girls in those days.

She told her parents she wanted to be a minister, and her father went with her to the church headquarters in Halifax. The official there was sympathetic, but told her kindly that the Presbyterian Church was not ready to accept women ministers.

Florence then decided to be a doctor and her parents promised to do all they could to help. They sent two daughters and four sons to Dalhousie University, and on a minister's salary of $750 a year, this meant a real sacrifice.

As time went on, missionaries from Korea and other countries came to the manse and she listened to their stories with fascination, especially Dr. Kate MacMillan's accounts of her life as a medical missionary in the Far East.

After graduating from Prince of Wales College in Charlottetown, Florence entered medical school in 1914, shortly after the outbreak of World War I. She was the only woman in a class which gradually shrank as the young men joined the forces and went to war.

On December 6, 1917, during her fourth year, the Halifax explosion devastated the town, leaving 1,500 people dead and thousands injured. The senior medical students were called in to help tend the countless numbers of patients crowded into make-shift dressing stations and tents, in blizzard conditions.

She later recalled that December morning when the shock and blast of an exploding munitions ship was heard as far away as Truro.

> Suddenly, the house shook, the windows blew in. I went outside and found people streaming with blood. The nearby druggist gave me, without question, all the supplies I needed. From there, I walked to Camp Hill Hospital, where already there were 1,500 emergencies in a building equipped for 100 convalescents. I helped administer morphine until it was all used up.

Florence was called on to help with surgery and told to give the anaesthetics. She had never given an anaesthetic before and she was terrified, but felt it was no time to make excuses.

Her first patient was six years old. She did not know how large or small a dose of ether to give. "I knew I should watch the eye reflexes to help judge the depth of anaesthesia. But this unfortunate child had lost both eyes."

She did so well that the next day Florence, now in her fourth year as a medical student, was appointed official anaesthetist in the hectic, overcrowded hospital.

A few weeks later another emergency arose when the Spanish influenza epidemic struck the Maritimes in full force. It was to kill 20 to 30 million people as it ran its worldwide course.

She was sent to Lockeport, a small fishing village where twenty-five people had died and the doctor had become ill. She had neither equipment nor a licence to practise, but the public health official who had called her said that he knew that. There was no one else to send. She could use the local doctor's equipment.

No one knew what to do for it. I went down with a stethoscope and thermometer. Later they sent me two nurses, one of whom took the flu. The Orange Hall was made into a hospital. Many complications arose—pneumonia, encephalitis and miscarriages were common.... I drove into the outlying district. Wherever there was a towel hung on the door, I found a flu victim,

One Lockeport native bitterly proclaimed, "No petticoat doctor is coming near me." When he became ill, he changed his mind.

There were no further deaths from influenza after Florence Murray's arrival; and few medical students have graduated as rich in experience as she did in 1919, but she was in debt and needed to earn money to pay her college bills.

The only hospital in Nova Scotia which paid interns was the Victoria General in Halifax and the superintendent was a businessman with no use for women interns, no matter how capable. So she went to Long Island Hospital in Boston where she was paid $11 a week in addition to room and board.

She was so distressed at the low standard of medical care and the lack of consideration for the patients that she took a weekend off and went to Halifax to ask advice from Dr. J.G. MacDougall with whom she had worked in her final year. She accepted his offer of a position as his assistant, she was also allowed to take private patients, and soon afterwards, she obtained a position as a demonstrator in anatomy in Dalhousie Medical School.

In a short time she had paid her debts and then she informed the Mission Board of the Canadian Presbyterian Church she was ready to go overseas. In 1921, Dr. Florence Murray went to Korea.

She needed to learn the language, but before she had finished, language study, the mission station in Yongjung, Manchuria, needed a doctor urgently as the resident missionary doctor, Newfoundlander Dr. Stanley Martin, was ill and was going on furlough.

Manchuria was mostly populated by Koreans who had been moved to Manchuria and Siberia in 1910 when Japan annexed Korea and forced many Koreans off their land. There were also resident Chinese and Japanese, as well as Russians who had fled from their homeland at the time of the 1917 revolution.

Florence had a Korean, a Chinese and a Japanese interpreter, but none of the Russians spoke English, and these people were undernourished and ill, and were pitiful sights to the young woman who was trying to cure them.

There was another problem there. Florence wrote:

> The nurses didn't like to nurse Russian patients and I once had to reprimand them for not being kinder to one.
>
> "We can't stand the smell of them," they protested.
>
> "Smell!" I exclaimed. "They won't smell if you keep them clean."
>
> "All the Russians smell awful. We hate to go near them. They all smell like weasels."
>
> "Like weasels, do they? If foreigners smell, we must smell too."
>
> "What do Dr. Martin and I smell like?" I demanded to know.
>
> This was embarrassing but they finally admitted that we smelled like cows.
>
> "Don't you drink milk and eat butter and cheese?" they pointed out."

Most of her contact, however, was with Koreans and Florence faced a patient load of 22,000 per year as well as the culture shock of the primitive life of these people, particularly the women, many of whom did not even have names. Girl children were valued so little that they might simply be addressed as "Hi you," or as "Back Room" if they happened to have been born in a back room.

She found that Korean women were not allowed to eat with the men, and the Chinese women in the population were crippled physically as well as socially. Although the practice of binding the feet was beginning to die out in China, it was still carried on in Manchuria. It caused great pain when the process was first begun on little girls. Florence was appalled when she saw the bound feet, the toes bent under the sole and the heels forced forward, until the grown women might have feet only four inches long.

Medically, the scene was also disturbing. Florence found many diseases rampant that were already under control in North America: typhoid, typhus, diphtheria, leprosy, malaria, sprue, parasites of all kinds, and especially tuberculosis.

Local medicine men treated patients by the *chim* and *doom* methods.

Chim was a crude acupuncture method of inserting cold or red-hot needles into the flesh, causing infections or burns which complicated her task as a surgeon. *Doom* consisted of placing piles of powdered leaves of certain plants on the skin over the affected area and then igniting them. This might be done over and over again on the one ulcerating spot. Florence asked one patient how many times she had had *doom* treatment and the answer was one hundred. It was not hard to believe as the treatment had penetrated skin and tissue into the muscular layer.

Even hospitality could be a problem for a Western doctor. Florence once made a house call on a Chinese who was ill with tuberculosis. She happened to know that the patient's brother was also ill in the same house. He had syphilis, in an infective stage.

> At the house, instead of going at once to see the sick man, we (she and an interpreter, Kim) were invited to sit down in an outer room where the hospitable master of the house lighted the family pipe and handed it to me. I didn't know what Chinese etiquette decreed in such cases and feared it might be taken as a slight if I refused. Even had I been a smoker, the family pipe in that house would have had no attraction for me. I declined as politely as I could.
>
> The man then lighted a cigarette, took a puff to get it going well, and passed it to me. Again, at the risk of giving offence, I had to decline. He then emptied the used teacups on to the floor, poured fresh hot tea, and gave cups to us. Kim accepted this. Fearing to decline a third time, in spite of unhappy thoughts about the infectious diseases in the household, I forced myself to swallow a few drops. The hardships that friends of overseas missionaries sometimes deplore are often more subtle than they imagine.

After a few years in Manchuria, Florence was asked to take over the hospital in Hamheung, Korea, where Dr. Kate MacMillan had been. It had been closed since Dr. MacMillan's death from typhus, and it needed many alterations to comply with building construction laws.

This was a job for which a medical education had not trained her. She set to work to make scale drawings, supervise the widening of corridors, moving of partitions, installation of wiring and plumbing, and building of a new operating room.

She sent for a graduate nurse and shortly after her arrival the young woman had a lung haemorrhage, admitted to having tuberculosis and then went home.

Dr. Murray's language teacher and her interpreter both left to go to medical school, so she had to get a new language teacher, Lee Sunsaing, who later became her secretary, purchasing agent for the hospital, business manager and when they acquired a sterilizer, he ran that too.

She wrote:

> He still bears the scars of his devotion to duty when one day the gasoline stove for heating the apparatus blew up and he carried the flaming equipment outdoors in his bare hands...
>
> I decided to have Lee Sunsaing give the anaesthetic while I operated. The first time, I explained to him what to do and what to look out for, since he had never even seen an anaesthetic administered.
>
> I started the anaesthesia myself and when the patient was well under the influence, I turned him over to Lee Sunsaing. Then I scrubbed up and did the operation with one eye on the surgery, the other on the anaesthetic. Both were successful, and Lee became the official anaesthetist for the hospital. During the 20 years he acted in that capacity he never had a fatality.

Running the hospital in Hamheung in the face of primitive cultural customs was never easy for Florence; she had to cope with lights which could fail during an operation; Chinese doctors were found doing their practice in her hospital; and always patients came who had had spirits mercilessly exorcised by a *mudang*'s sorcery, or by a "specialist" in *chim* and *doom*.

> The torture meted out by travelling old crones who professed to cure women suffering from neglected complications of childbirth was barbarous. Subjected to unwise treatment by ignorant midwives, these women were expected to get up as soon as the baby was born and go to the river to wash the soiled clothing.
>
> The heavy uterus often sagged down into the dilated birth canal which resulted in permanent displacement which in turn led to other difficulties. Some victims could neither sit nor walk comfortably. Too modest or too impecunious to go to a hospital, they patronized the ignorant creatures who preyed upon their misfortune. Usually, only after much suffering and further complications, did they finally seek sensible treatment.

On two occasions, Florence bought girls who had been sold to a brothel by distant relatives in order to save them from their fate.

They both went to Salvation Army homes where they were taught to read, write, sew and learn the Christian way of life.

Then came the Great Depression and the home churches were unable to send more missionaries and had to cut the salaries of the staff already in the field. Nevertheless, Florence's staff remained loyal and continued working in the hospital.

In 1935, Florence returned to Canada for a year's furlough and returned in 1936 to find a new assistant surgeon with no experience in surgery in her hospital.

In 1937, Japan provoked war with China and conditions in Korea became very tense, and every house and institution was required to black out all windows and doors. They carried on in the hospital and, with difficulty, continued to make home visits to the sick. Then came December 7, 1941, and the United States entered World War II after the Japanese bombed Pearl Harbour. Their lives were changed irrevocably thereafter.

Florence and the mission staff were put under house arrest, although she and her nurses were allowed to go to the hospital which now had one hundred beds.

Towards the end of May 1942, they were told to be ready to go to Tokyo as they were to be exchanged for Japanese prisoners and repatriated. On June 1, carrying their hand luggage and on foot, they were marched to the railway station and journeyed by night to go aboard a ship in which they travelled, below decks, to Japan.

Florence had written the story of her life in Korea and Manchuria, as well as many other articles, but she never saw them again. There were ninety-nine repatriates in the group taken to Kobe, Japan, where the Canadians and Americans were kept, twelve in a room fifteen feet by eighteen feet for two weeks. Their diet was mostly raw fish and cabbage. Their time was spent being lined up and counted by their captors.

After another overnight train journey, they boarded the *Asama Maru* at Yokohama, bound for Hong Kong, Saigon, Singapore and Lourenco Marques in Portuguese East Africa, where the Swedish liner *Gripsholm* welcomed the 1,500 prisoners heading for freedom. There were shouts of delight when they were served white bread, real butter, fresh fruit, vegetables and roast fowl.

On August 25, 1942, they arrived in New York harbour, and that night, a sealed and guarded train took the sixty-nine repatriated Canadians to Montreal.

Florence spent the rest of the war in Halifax and Kentville, in practice. In 1947 she was allowed to return to Korea to be associate dean of the Women's University Medical Faculty in Seoul. But in 1950, she was again forced to leave the country because of the Korean War.

The following year she returned to find the port of Pusan swarming with sick refugees. The stores had been turned into military hospitals for wounded soldiers. There was no place for sick civilians. She found one nurse caring for sixty patients under the most primitive conditions.

In port there was a Danish Red Cross ship where 400 wounded soldiers were being cared for, but none of the medical or nursing staff could speak Korean. Dr. Murray went aboard and discovered they had 200 vacant beds.

They arranged an exchange. Dr. Murray would act as an interpreter (her Korean was fluent) and she would have use of the 200 hospital beds for civilians.

Her time was filled with care for her patients in the city of Pusan, crowded with refugees from the war, and without fail she went aboard the hospital ship each day.

The Korean soldiers welcomed the doctor who could speak to them in their own language. "I went every day. I was doctor, interpreter, errand boy and grandmother to the boys," she said.

In 1961, after forty years of service in Korea, she retired from the United Church Overseas staff. But this was not the end of service in Korea for Florence Murray.

She had always wanted to do something for leprosy patients and their families, and so she found new challenges among the abject, rejected leprosy outcasts, reviled by all people in Korea.

In a letter written in late 1964, she described the conditions inflicted on leprosy sufferers.

> One patient did her best after the death of her husband to make a living by gathering fuel on the mountain behind her house where she lived apart from everyone else. Youths who also gathered fuel on the mountain cursed and stoned her to drive her away. Finally, to get rid of her, they burned down her house, leaving her without a roof over her head; one result of ignorance and prejudice.

She visited a patient in a village who asked her to cut off his foot... She refused and asked him to try her method of treatment for ten days and if his foot were not better, then she would discuss amputation.

In ten days he was able to walk and he told his friends, "That old grandmother knows something." As the word spread, the victims of leprosy asked for a clinic. An old army tent was set up and the first clinic was started, only to be destroyed when it was blown down in a gale. They then moved to an old storehouse.

A unit of the U.S. army helped by hauling sand and gravel to a site for a new dispensary, building materials were donated and the patients built their own clinic, and from the material left over they built a little chapel. Later they erected a monument to Dr. Florence Murray beside the chapel.

In 1965, Florence went to Severance Hospital in Seoul to reorganize the medical records and train people to continue the work. The outpatient records, more than 40,000 a year, had not been filed for eleven years. Records prior to that date had been destroyed in the Korean War.

In 1967, with the records up to date and in order, she retired and returned to Nova Scotia to re-write the story of her first twenty years in Korea. It was published under the title, *At the Foot of Dragon Hill*.

For her lifetime of courageous service, she received honorary degrees from Pine Hill College and from Dalhousie University; the President of Korea awarded her the Order of Civil Merit, and, for her service aboard the Danish Red Cross hospital ship, she was awarded a gold medal by the King of Denmark.

At the age of eighty, she made her final journey to Korea to visit her old friends. In 1975, the following year, she died suddenly, revered by all her friends as a great lady, a dedicated servant of mankind, and a magnificent doctor.

As a young woman, Florence had said, "I want to use my life where it will count most," and towards the end of her life, she said with typical modesty, "Such a checkered career surely makes one a jack-of-all-trades and master of none, but no-one has had more satisfaction in it than I."

Annie Almira Anderson,

a graduate in 1920, was born on October 8, 1889, to Captain and Mrs. W.F. Gilchrist of Moser River, Nova Scotia. While still a child, her family moved to western Canada and she was brought up on a cattle ranch.

She was twenty-one years old when she married W. Anderson in 1911 and they went to live at Fort Walsh, Saskatchewan. Within a year, he had died, and his young widow, an unusually beautiful woman, returned to Nova Scotia. She registered at Dalhousie University and studied medicine.

One month after graduating, she married Major Hugh A. Dickson, and they lived at Onslow and Truro. They had a daughter and two sons.

For many years, Dr. Annie Dickson was prominent in public health work. She was provincial convener for health in the Women's Institute, and the Home and School Federation of Nova Scotia, and took a leading part in the Victorian Order of Nurses, Truro Hospital Auxiliary and the Imperial Order Daughters of the Empire.

Her husband served in two world wars, and their eldest son, named for his father, Hugh, Jr., served in the RCAF. He was

Dr. Dickson after retirement.

reported missing in September 1942. Her husband was invalided home in 1945, and three years later he died. Annie was a widow for the second time.

The following summer, in July 1949, she went to Mount Allison as dean of women and lecturer in physiology. Her qualities were quickly perceived and appreciated by the students, one of whom wrote:

> Here's a salute to the most wonderful dean a women's residence could ever have. Scintillating with enthusiasm, bubbling with friendliness and charm, genuine and motherly. Dr. Dickson has won the heart and confidence of every girl in the U.G.R.
>
> Although she was entirely new to residence life, before the first month was over, she had learned the idiosyncrasies of even the most eccentric seniors and the names of all the freshettes. Always eager to help, sympathetic to listen, gentle to chide. May her stay here be happy and lengthy, for she's an example of a true lady and a wonderful dean.

On her retirement, after ten years as dean of women, she was given an honorary degree by Mount Allison University.

A fellow professor said at the ceremony,

Few women in the Maritime Provinces have contributed more to community activities than Dr. Dickson. For many years she was provincial convener for health for both the Home and School Federation and the Women's Institute. On behalf of these organizations she travelled widely through the province and was well known to many Nova Scotians as an able platform speaker. Dr. Dickson, with her medical education and experience with young people and with her interests in the United Church, the community, education and in people, brought a rich and varied background to her position at Mount Allison. During her 10 years here, as a wise counsellor to hundreds of women students, as an excellent teacher, and as the gracious hostess of Allison Hall, she has made a fine contribution to the life of this University.

In a letter dated February 22, 1989, her son wrote:

One of her main traits and perhaps the one that has controlled much of her life is simply: let bygones be bygones and let's get on with the future. She was an avid traveller until she was stalled at 85 by her bad back.... Mother enjoyed learning and might well have gone into research had she chosen to do so.

Her chief memory of student days at Dalhousie is of the debating group which included Dr. Florence Murray; and at the age of ninety-nine, Dr. Dickson was confined to a wheelchair, living in Calgary, in remarkably good shape, according to her son Archie, and expecting to "make it" to her one hundredth birthday in the fall of 1989, and she did.

Ella Pearl Hopgood

graduated in 1920. She became one of Canada's outstanding psychiatrists, and an organizer and supervisor of St. John Ambulance in Nova Scotia. She was widely known for her work in the treatment of mental illness.

The year she graduated, she joined the staff of the Nova Scotia Hospital and was made assistant superintendent in 1928. She was one of the first woman doctors in North America to become an executive in an institution for the care and treatment of psychiatric patients.

Through most of her career she directed the teaching of nurses at the Nova Scotia Hospital and she combined the then newly advanced application of psychiatry to her treatment of patients at the institution.

During the period leading up to the war of 1939-45 she was active as a lecturer and examiner in first aid and home nursing, and when war came, she was appointed divisional surgeon for one of the nursing divisions of St. John Ambulance Brigade.

In March 1948, Dr. Hopgood was appointed provincial superintendent of nursing divisions in Nova Scotia. Her outstanding work in the Order of St. John was recognized, and in September 1949, the Governor General of Canada awarded her a Priory Vote of Thanks. She was made a Commander of the Order of St. John, the oldest order of chivalry in the Commonwealth, and was invested in Ottawa by Lord Alexander of Tunis, Governor General of Canada.

On recommendation of the Ambulance committee in London, England, Dr. Hopgood was awarded an honorary life membership in St. John Ambulance Association.

Dr. Hopgood held several offices in HMS *Shannon* Chapter of the Imperial Order Daughters of the Empire, of which she was secretary for six years. She served as president of the Halifax branch of the Business and Professional Women's Club; she was a charter member of the Nova Scotia branch of the Federation of Medical Women of Canada and its president in 1928, a member of the Medical Society of Nova Scotia and the American Psychiatric Association.

She retired in 1953, and in 1956 took over as temporary administrator of the Cape Breton County Hospital, and on May 1, 1956, she was presented with a shield by the Canadian Mental Health Association for outstanding service to the field of mental health. Dr. Hopgood died on March 8, 1957.

Mabel Patterson

was forty years old when she graduated in the class of 1921. She was born in Pictou County in 1881, and, after graduating from Pictou Academy, taught school for several years before entering Dalhousie Medical School.

She interned in Saint John General Hospital and, in spite of fears that a woman intern would not do her work properly, she proved to be a very busy and satisfactory intern, paving the way for the women doctors who followed her. She returned to Nova Scotia and was a busy general practitioner for more than fifty years in Dartmouth.

A tall, stately woman with a regal stature, she was active in community affairs, especially the Imperial Order Daughters of the Empire. She supported the Federation of Medical Women of Canada, was a charter member of the Nova Scotia Branch and was president of the Federation in 1938-39.

In 1980, Dr. Patterson was ninety-nine years old when Dr. Enid MacLeod visited her and spoke of her approaching one hundredth birthday. The old lady said, "Enid, I've had a good life and I'm tired—I'd rather not live long enough to be 100." But she lived on for two more years.

In 1989, two of Dr. Patterson's former patients were asked for their opinion of her as a physician. Mrs. M.G. Dauphinee wrote:

> Dr. Mabel Patterson became my family doctor shortly after my marriage in July 1932, and she was in all respects a wonderful and dedicated physician.
>
> Dr Patterson delivered my three daughters in my home at 212 Windmill Road. The first, in 1933, was a breech birth; the second in 1936, the third in 1938, and our only son in 1944 at the Halifax Infirmary.
>
> In the Spring of 1939 I was stricken with a mastoid ear, Dr. Patterson was called and she immediately came to our home and, after a quick but thorough examination, she realized a surgeon was needed immediately. She called Dr. Doull at once and he came over to Dartmouth by the next ferry. After one quick look he said there was not time to get to the hospital, so he operated on the mastoid in the bedroom of our home. It was only by the quick action of Dr. Patterson who ably assisted Dr. Doull that my life was spared.
>
> Dr. Patterson continued as my family doctor until she retired.

Another former patient, Mrs. Winnie Bateman of Dartmouth, said Dr. Patterson was the personal physician of her and her mother.

On many occasions, Dr Patterson's sense of humour added to her popularity. Mrs. Bateman's mother once said to Dr. Patterson, "I am glad you came as I always feel so good when you've gone." Dr. Patterson enjoyed the joke.

Three of Mrs. Bateman's children were born at home at Port Wallis. Once on a very stormy winter night she started labour, and Dr. Patterson had great difficulty driving horse and sleigh to Port Wallis, and was almost forced off the Red Bridge on the way. She finally arrived and stayed the night. After the baby was delivered the next morning she told Mrs. Bateman that she had been kept awake because Mr. Bateman had snored all night, and asked her how she ever managed to get any sleep.

Dr. Patterson died in a nursing home at the age of 101, in 1982.

Mildred Resnick

was born in Lower Economy in 1897 and was in the class of 1921 at Dalhousie Medical School. After graduation, she interned in Kentville Sanatorium and then worked in Montreal, doing blood work among the veterans of World War I. Following this, she went to Glasgow, Scotland, and worked under Dr. Finley, a paediatrician, studying children's diseases, and later as an observer in London, England.

In 1924, she married Joseph Cyril Glube and settled in Halifax, and from this time until 1930, Dr. Glube practised as a paediatrician in Halifax. She was very active in the social life of the city, and she stopped practising medicine because "women in medicine were not socially acceptable." She became active in social work and the Women's Council until 1941.

During World War II, there was a need for anaesthetists in Halifax as many of the doctors had gone overseas, so Dr. Glube went to the Poly-Clinic in New York to study anaesthesia. On her return to Nova Scotia, she worked as an anaesthetist and was the first person to use an anaesthetic machine and to do endotracheal intubation in Halifax. She retired in 1952. She died in February 1990.

Graduates of 1922: (clockwise from top) Grace Cragg, Elizabeth Thurrott, Anna Creighton and Christena MacLeod

Grace Theresa Mary Cragg

was one of four women in the class of 1922 at Dalhousie Medical School. She was born in 1899, the seventh of ten children born to a prominent Halifax merchant, Francis Cragg and Rose Cornelia (Patton) Cragg.

As a girl, she attended the Convent of the Sacred Heart and was a top student, talented and actively involved in music and drama with a special interest in literature. She was twenty-three years old when she graduated from Dalhousie Medical School, and took up residence in the United States. She pursued a career in the relatively new field of psychiatry, and first worked in the State Hospital in Concord, New Hampshire. Thereafter she was appointed staff psychiatrist at Medfield State Hospital, Massachusetts

Dr. Cragg retired to Franklin, Massachusetts, in 1955 and provided consultative service at Valleyhead Hospital, Concord. In 1962, she married Charles Vasaturo, who died a year later. She was always a keen gardener and a long-time member of the American Garden Society—well known for her expertise in growing prize-winning gladioli. She died in 1980, in Miami, Florida.

Christena Catherine MacLeod

was born in 1901 in North Sydney, Cape Breton, a daughter of Murdoch and Effie MacLeod. She entered Dalhousie Medical School when she was only fifteen years old, "with her hair hanging down her back and very naive," she said. She graduated at the age of twenty-one in 1922.

She interned at the Saint John General Hospital, and at the Halifax Children's Hospital with her classmate Elizabeth Thurrot. Then, as was usual in those days, if a Canadian woman wished to get a residency, she went to the United States, and so did Tena, as she was known.

She interned at the Worcester Hospital, Massachusetts, and then went on to Bellevue Hospital in New York, which had been taking woman interns since World War I. She did post-graduate training in anaesthesia.

Her career was interrupted when she contracted tuberculosis and had to take the treatment of those days—prolonged rest in bed with fresh air and good food. Tena spent several years in the sanatorium at River Glade, New Brunswick, and she was still convalescing when she became a member of the staff at the Glades—an appointment she held until 1945.

After her cure, she specialized in treating tuberculosis and was assistant physician at the Jordan Memorial Sanatorium at the Glades, New Brunswick. One of her patients was Donald Mac-Lauchlan, PhD, a Rhodes Scholar, who later became professor of chemistry and dean of men at Mount Allison University.

The physician and patient fell in love, were married and lived happily in Sackville, New Brunswick. Dr. MacLeod had complications following a hip fracture and died on April 20, 1985, at the age of eighty-four years.

Elizabeth Hope Thurrott,

a graduate of Dalhousie in 1922, (known as Bessie) was born in 1892 in Newcastle Bridge, New Brunswick. She was the fourth of thirteen children born to staunch Presbyterian parents of Scottish and Irish stock. As a child, she wanted to become a medical missionary in India, and she never lost sight of that goal.

She was an asthmatic girl, and her poor health forced her to complete her high-school studies by correspondence. She graduated from Normal School at the top of her class and then went to the University of New Brunswick for one year.

After graduation from Dalhousie Medical School, MDCM, she interned at the Children's Hospital, Halifax, for six months and then at the Saint John General Hospital, New Brunswick, for two years.

At about this time, the Women's Union Missionary Society of America put out an urgent call for women doctors to go to India. The society was interdenominational and international, with headquarters in New York, and its slogan was, "Women's work, for Women, by Women."

Bessie felt the call was meant for her, but she felt she could not go until her debts were paid. An aged doctor who was interested in missionary work offered to pay her debts. Bessie accepted, and Bessie sailed for India on January 12, 1925, and for the next six years she was in charge of the society's sixty-bed hospital in Jhansi.

She learned the language and studied the character, disposition, outlook and mental attitude of the people among whom she was living. Bessie grew to love the people of India, especially the very poor, illiterate, ignorant, despised, low-caste villager.

In Jhansi there was one physician to 9,000 patients, while in the villages there were thousands of people who were visited by missionaries only occasionally, and villages where no missionary lived.

When her furlough came due, she resigned from the missionary society, went home to Canada, took a course at Moody Bible Institute and returned to India in 1932 to work for the Women's Missionary Society of the Presbyterian Church.

For two years she travelled from one village to another by bicycle, and in 1934 she persuaded the mission to let her live in Babina, a market town with a population of 3,000, lying nineteen miles south of Jhansi.

She was determined to be an evangelist first and a doctor second. She gathered the people together by singing, and after preaching and praying she would tend the sick who were brought to her, leaving medicine for the medical cases and sending the surgical cases to hospital.

The Hindus seemed to resent her at first, but later became friendly and she was known as "Babina Missionary Lady." She obtained the services of John and Samuel Kashi Nath, two brothers who were trained evangelists, to accompany her on her travels, by bicycle, to outlying villages.

During the war, Babina was a military camp for heavy artillery training, the military school of hygiene and a training camp for the African and Indian pioneer corps. There was no padre for these thousands of troops, so Bessie and her co-workers held religious services for the men.

In 1966, she officially retired and returned briefly to Canada, but India still held its fascination and she went back to work until 1979, this time independently among the villagers. In her eighty-seventh year she had a stroke, and Dr. Bessie Thurrott returned to her New Brunswick birthplace, where she was found to have cancer. She died February 19, 1980.

Grace Cragg, her classmate, wrote at the time of her death: "She is one of the unsung heroines who devoted her life to the needs of others ..." Her niece, Mary Thurrott, said her Aunt Bessie had a pioneering spirit, she was a woman of prayer and she practised her faith. "Wherever there was a need, there you would find her."

Anna St. Clair Creighton

graduated in 1922. When she wrote her autobiography in 1984, she called it *My Father's Reply*, and explained it in this manner:

> As a young woman, I wanted to study medicine but was afraid that if I asked my father, he would give a resounding "No!"
>
> One day, my cousin Florence Murray saved me from asking. She said to my father, "Would you have any objections to Anna studying medicine?"
>
> For one brief moment I held my breath. His answer was "She may take any course she wishes as long as she can earn an honest living at it." My mother exacted one promise from me—that I was not to talk about my medical studies at home.

She entered the medical school in 1917, and was soon good friends with her classmates, Tena MacLeod, Grace Cragg, and Elizabeth Thurrott. The four young women often did their studying together.

The Halifax Explosion occurred a few months after they had entered medical school and even first year students were called on to help in caring for the injured.

Dr. Anna Laing (left) visited her classmate Dr. Bess Thurrott and neice, Mary Thurrott, in India c. 1963)

The whole class was given something to do; some students gave tetanus shots to victims; Anna was sent to the new military hospital which had been built, but had no equipment or beds, and she was told to help set fractured bones and suture wounds.

After two weeks working with the casualties, classes were resumed, and the class of '22 did not see or have contact with patients again until their third year.

After graduation, she followed Mabel Patterson as an intern in Saint John General Hospital. They changed services every three months and the board of governors inspected the hospital each month, even examining the bureau drawers and closets of the interns' rooms.

> One month they found three empty ginger ale bottles in each of the boy's closets... In my closet they found 13 empty bottles. Nothing was said openly, but my reputation was not helped any over this find.

During that year, insulin was discovered, and Anna recalled how thrilling it was in those early days to watch a high blood sugar curve down to normal and to see a life saved through insulin injections.

After her rotating internship, Anna felt she could not go into general practice without more training in obstetrics. She obtained a place in a hospital where one of her classmates had worked, but was subsequently denied the position because the former intern had returned. This rejection led to other events and her challenge of gender discrimination when she became a specialist in the male-dominated field of ophthalmology.

Anna had been interested in X-ray when she was at the Saint John General Hospital, so she wrote requesting to study with Dr. Carr in Dubuque, Iowa, and was accepted. At that time many radiologists failed to take proper precautions and lost fingers or hands due to overexposure to X-ray. Dr. Carr had trouble with her hands and arms and did not use water on them, they were too dry and crusty—this was the start of the complications which finally took her life. Anna, too, experienced similar problems with her hands.

After six months, Dr. Carr arranged for Anna to study radiology at Cook County Hospital, Chicago, where she would get a greater volume of cases. The day neared when she would leave for Chicago, when, to her surprise, a leading eye, ear, nose and throat specialist, Dr. Gratiot of Dubuque, asked if she would help him as second assistant. She took the job and stayed for two years, finding that she liked working on eyes better than anything.

Ophthalmology was just beginning to be considered a separate specialty from otolaryngology, and her applications for a residency in ophthalmology were rejected by all the large hospitals in the Union.

She was advised to go to New York and take any medical work she could find, and then she might get a residency in "eyes." She left for New York and obtained a residency in anaesthesia at Bellevue Hospital. It was probably the hardest year of her busy life.

Those were the days when the main anaesthetic was ether, and though she found the work demanding it was enjoyable. She dreaded most the cases of cleft-palate:

> Perhaps cleft-palate surgery is not as much of a trauma for surgeons now as it was in those long ago days. Everything but an undeclared war took place in the operating room the day this type of surgery was done.

When she was giving anaesthesia on eye service, the surgeon, Dr. Wheeler, would ask the boys to stand aside to let her see what was going on. She took this as a sign that he was aware of her interest, so she applied for a residency. She received no response and was on the point of giving up when she was told, "Dr. Wheeler is a queer man... Write to him again and ask for an interview."

The response was immediate and the surgeon went to Bellevue, took her to see his patients in the New York Eye and Ear Infirmary, and asked her if she could give orders to a man. She had to admit she had never done so. "That is the rub. A man will not take orders from a woman," he said.

She said farewell and thought about joining Dr. Thurrott in India, when, quite unexpectedly, she received a letter from Dr. Wheeler telling her to report to him as his resident in ophthalmology at Bellevue. She had broken a barrier, and became probably the first woman to graduate from an ophthalmology residency.

She spent seven months in the New York Eye and Ear Infirmary, but was unable to begin surgery there as her hands were still tender and bled if scrubbed. The next two years were spent at Kings County Hospital, Brooklyn, and at St. Vincent's Hospital Eye Clinic, where she performed the first cataract surgery she had done in three years. She told nobody how much her hands hurt, which was a result of her exposure to x-ray.

Before she could pass the American Board of Ophthalmology exams, she needed a certain number of glaucoma cases, so she joined St. Luke's Hospital and soon had enough experience to satisfy the board.

She worked three afternoons a week at St. Vincent's Hospital and another three at St Luke's, spending one afternoon a week in the operating room of each hospital. She needed a bread-and-butter job, so Dr. Anna Creighton, Ophthalmologist, opened an office on Forty-fourth Street, New York City, and saw enough patients in the evenings to pay the rent. Later she had an office in her home, but for many years, the city physicians did not give her the referrals she needed to build up even a modest practice.

Anna became well settled in New York, but her musician husband, James R. Laing, wanted to go upstate to Rochester. They tossed a coin, and they went to Rochester. Dr. Anna gave up her New York hospital connections, took a job with Eastman-Kodak, maintained her practice in Amityville, commuting to New York weekly, and did eye surgery at the Rochester General Hospital. She also taught clinical ophthalmology at Strong Memorial Hospital, Rochester.

Five years later, World War II had ended and they moved back to New York. She opened an office on Sixty-first Street and worked in the eye service at the New York Eye and Ear Infirmary for the next twenty years.

In 1959, she was invited to go to a mission hospital in what was then known as the French Cameroons. She was in France, en route, when she received a telegram:

> Much violence here. Roads blocked. Many people killed. Proceed at your own risk. We thought you should be told. Contact Dr. Chazeaud. He will advise.

She thought that having gone so far it would be an anticlimax to go back home, and she consulted Dr. Chazeaud. He had not heard of the violence and he gave her a box of artificial eyes, a gift from a New York firm, and put her on a plane for the Cameroons. When she opened the box, she saw that all the eyes were blue!

Arriving at Douala at 6 a.m., she found the airport was guarded by African soldiers with fixed bayonets. On a smaller plane bound for Yaounde a fellow passenger proved to be the minister of health in his district and on arriving, he helped her to cut through the local red tape.

At the mission station, she learned of the atrocities and killings of the previous week. The airport had been the scene of a skirmish and had been bloodied from floor to ceiling. The first two rows of people at a theatre in Douala had been decapitated. An emergency meeting was held to discuss what the hospital staff should do if the hospital were attacked. She later wrote,

> If it had not been serious, it would have been ludicrous. Several suggestions were made, one of which almost made me laugh; that we should all arm ourselves with large brown paper bags and blow them up with air and at a given signal break them, causing a bang that could frighten the terrorists.

During the talks, the group was alarmed by the sound of gunfire outside. Two people cautiously went out to investigate and found two Portuguese sailors shooting at birds.

One of Dr. Anna's patients in eye surgery was the Cameroons' minister of telecommunications, a man aged only thirty-two years but with mature cataracts in both eyes. He arrived in a limousine with six armed guards, each with a machete, a rifle and hand pistols, and they stationed themselves in his room and outside the door.

When the mission's chief doctor was showing an African male nurse how to raise the head of the bed, two pistols slid from under the blind patient's pillow. Dr. Anna had to stop herself from laughing out loud.

With two armed guards in sterile capes on each side of her, she operated on the minister of telecommunications, and when the cataracts were removed, the man shouted out in French and in the African dialect, "I can see! I can see!" He was so excited that Anna had to have the guards calm him in case he had a haemorrhage there and then. When he was wheeled out of surgery, she could hear him shouting all the way back to his room, "I can see."

Anna was fascinated with the Cameroons and writes,

> One of the things that made me tingle all over when I was in the Cameroons was the talking drums. They were used instead of Church bells. The year before I visited the Cameroons, a woman missionary had been murdered. It happened the only night her husband had to be away for twenty-four hours. An African village sixty miles away knew the story via the drums before her friends knew at the hospital, only six miles away.

The week after Anna left, two tons of dynamite were found in the jungle near the hospital.

In 1962, her husband suffered a severe cerebral haemorrhage. After his death, Dr. Anna fulfilled a commitment to go to India to do eye surgery at a mission hospital. She was accompanied by the younger of her two sons, Ian. They went to a hospital camp at Guru Harsai, where an ophthalmologist was sorely needed. At dawn on her first morning at the eye clinic, she found more than 300 people waiting to be seen. Anna treated them all as though they were private patients.

She continued to practise medicine for twenty more years in Amityville, and, in 1982, she completed her autobiography.

In 1982, her colleague, Dr. Hampton A. Sisler, wrote,

> The first woman resident in that area of medicine (ophthalmology) at New York City's famous Bellevue Hospital, Anna Creighton Laing, MD, is a person greatly to be admired. Having triumphed

over the antiwoman prejudices of her day by her superior personality and conscientious performance, Dr. Laing set a truly fine example.... Continuing in that true pioneering spirit, she repeated that "first" when she courageously went to ... the French Cameroons, against precautionary advice....

Anna possesses the ability to parry a sceptical reception with grace and dignity, winning her way slowly but certainly through her altruism, her gentle manner and her ophthalmic skills. God bless Bellevue's first lady of ophthalmology.

Dalhousie University, conferred on her an honorary degree in 1985. Now aged 90, Dalhousie's pioneering woman ophthalmologist, who restored sight to so many people, is almost blind and lives still at Amityville.

Margaret Rebecca Chase

graduated in 1923. Born in 1896, she was the daughter of Oscar Chase, Port Williams, Kings County, where she had her early education. Margaret graduated with a bachelor of arts degree from Acadia University in 1918 and entered Dalhousie Medical School.

After graduation and a period of internship in Philadelphia, she was appointed a staff member of a medical institute in upper New York State.

She married Dr. Ross Collins in September 1927, and went with him to Edmonton in 1930 when he was appointed professor of history at the University of Alberta.

During World War II, she was associated with Dr. Mary Hunter in the management of the Red Cross Blood Donor Clinic. In the same period, she assisted in the administration of anaesthesia at University Hospital, Edmonton.

After the war, she conducted a well-baby clinic for the city's health department and was associated with Dr. Mildred Newell in the practice of medicine, from which she retired in 1963.

Her twenty years of service to the Edmonton branch of the Canadian Red Cross Society were recognized in 1963, when she was made an honorary life member of the society.

She remained a member of the society's council and executive, and chairman of its swimming and water safety committee. She was also a life member of the Federation of Medical Women of Canada and the Women's University Club.

She died in Edmonton on November 11, 1977, after a long period of ill health. She had one daughter, Mary, and two sons, Alan and Malcolm. Her sister was Dr. Lillian Chase, a graduate of the University of Toronto, 1922; and a cousin was Dr. Lalia Chase, Dalhousie School of Medicine, class of 1924.

Alan, her son, wrote of his mother,

> From my standpoint, the most significant aspect of mother's career was the fact that she was a post-liberated woman, having successfully entered a male-dominated occupation, she realized that caring for children is the most important work in the world.
>
> I learned this lesson from her life as she was regularly present in our home to nurture me and my siblings during our pre-school years and in later years when we were home from school at noon and after school. While this is not a fashionable viewpoint at the present time, I do hope you will include this important information in mother's biography.

Phebe Kirsten Christianson

was one of two women among the twenty-three graduates in the class of 1923.

She was born on September 5, 1897, in Glace Bay, Cape Breton, the only child of a mining engineer, Peter Christianson and Catherine McKeigan Christianson.

In 1910, her father's work took them to Edmonton and later to the foothills of the Rockies where he was superintendent of a Pacific Pass mine. She completed high school in Alberta, after which her family moved back to Nova Scotia and settled in North Sydney.

Phebe took a business course in Sydney and, like so many of her contemporaries, she became a stenographer and she was employed at the Nova Scotia Steel and Coal Company. Then a conference in Wolfville changed her life. She travelled to the university town in Annapolis Valley to attend the meeting and met Florence Murray and other women doctors. She was inspired by them, and resolved there and then to become a doctor.

She had to study at nights and on weekends to make up her deficiencies. At high school, Phebe had taken French and German instead of Latin, and she was weak in geometry, algebra, chemistry and physics. In 1918, at age twenty-one she was admitted to medical school.

During her first year, she lived with other women students in a residence for Dalhousie girls on the first floor of Halifax Ladies College. The Halifax explosion had occurred the previous year, and many damaged churches and offices were still boarded up.

In 1918, Phebe experienced one of the most memorable events in her life. It was Armistice Day, the end of World War I.

> On the early morning of November 11, 1918, when the clear sky was still full of stars, all the church bells started to ring. We all knew what it meant. The thrill was actually physical as well as mental. The College provided us with a hasty breakfast, and we all made for the centre of town, to celebrate.

In 1920, her father was dying and she went home for a time. On her return, she lived with the family of the Rev. S.S. Thompson at 24 Church Street. (Phebe and Willard Owen Thompson, MD, Harvard, 1923, one of the family's four sons, were married June 21, 1923.)

In 1921, her mother sold the family home in Sydney Mines, rented a house next to Studley athletic field, South Street, and took in boarders; among them were Marion Irving and Margaret Chase, who also became doctors.

Phebe was a member of the Delta Gamma Club, a society for Dalhousie women students who were interested in debating and literary pursuits. She belonged to the Student Christian Movement and met students from other disciplines, one of whom was Alex Kerr, who went on to become president of Dalhousie University from 1945 to 1963. She made friends with women doctors and other medical students who were not in her class, and still remembers Mildred Resnick, Florence Murray, Grace Cragg, Pearl Hopgood and Alice Thorne when they were young.

From 1922 to 1923, she interned in the Children's Hospital, Halifax and graduated MDCM, and went to the Harvard School of Public Health as an assistant in the biochemistry and applied physiology departments. She published her first article on the toxicology of zinc in the *Journal of Industrial Hygiene* in 1925, and when Willard completed his internship at Boston City Hospital in 1926, they both went to the metabolism laboratory in the thyroid clinic of Massachusetts General Hospital, Boston, where she was a research fellow in medicine.

In 1929, they went to Rush Medical College at the University of Chicago, always working together as a team. For the next sixteen years, she was assistant in the metabolism department in endocrinology at Rush Medical College and the Central Free Dispensary, Chicago.

Phebe was in private practice with her husband in Chicago from 1947 until he died suddenly in 1954. At the time of his death, the two youngest of their four children were beginning high school, so she deliberately chose the offered positions of editor of the *Journal of Clinical Endocrinology and Metabolism (JCEM)* and the *Journal of the American Geriatrics Society (JAGS)*. The work could be done in her own office at home, which was pertinent to her care of the two young children. "That was how I started being a medical editor," she wrote later.

Her editorship at the *JCEM* ended in 1964, and at *JAGS* in 1982 when she was eighty-four years of age.

Phebe was active in research during her early professional life and was sole author of four publications on the metabolism of zinc. She and her husband did thyroid studies on the effect of iodine and the treatment of Addison's disease, resulting in sixty-six more scientific papers of which she was co-author.

> Our joint papers, from 1928 on, were chiefly in endocrinology, beginning with the thyroid. Those were the days when the Mayo Clinic gained world-wide fame for Dr. Henry Plummer's discovery of how to apply pre-operative iodine therapy to calm the exophthalmic goitre patient and thus avoid the prevalent "thyroid storm" at the time of operation.
>
> We did many studies on the amount of iodine (surprisingly small) necessary to maintain this effect. We also did a great deal of work on myxoedema, e.g., iodine myxoedema and the full course of the effect of a dose of thyroxine intravenously.
>
> In Chicago, as the Midwest was no longer a "goitre belt," the focus of our work shifted to the newly discovered treatment of Addison's disease (lack of adrenal cortex hormone.) The hormone was delivered to us by Wilson Bros., Pharmaceutical Division, in quart bottles. The hormonal liquid was made by Wilson Laboratories directly from the adrenal glands of cattle they imported from Argentina.

It was amazingly effective. Soon the active ingredient was made synthetically, as cortisone. (President Kennedy received such treatment.) Also, we did a great deal of clinical work with the effects of both female and male sex hormones. This brought us in contact with other workers in the field from all over the world. Exciting days.

Then came the era of radio-iodine therapy and blood analyses instead of basal metabolic rates to measure oxygen consumption. We did some work with the new synthetic drugs. Then Willard Thompson died suddenly in March 1954.

At the age of ninety-two, Phebe Kirsten Thompson is still a busy woman living in Chicago, freelancing and intending to write a book about her native province, Nova Scotia.

Lalia Barclay Chase

graduated in 1924. She was born in Port Williams, a daughter of William Henry Chase, an apple and potato exporter. Her father, one of three brothers, was a descendant of one of the planter grantees who arrived in Nova Scotia in 1764 and settled in Kings County. This family was the only one which, before coming to Nova Scotia, belonged to the Society of Friends. Her father was wealthy and built and lived in what is now Victoria Inn in Wolfville.

Lalia and her brother both studied medicine, but he died young as a result of a brain tumour. Shortly after Lalia's graduation, her mother died and Lalia decided to stay at home and help her father in his business and be his hostess at home. She became a businesswoman in an arena occupied mainly by businessmen.

Lalia never practised medicine. However, she always maintained an active interest in medical affairs, read the various medical journals, and had financial participation in the local hospital at Wolfville, N.S. Her first cousins were Dr. Lillian Chase (Toronto 1922) and Dr. Margaret Chase Collins (Dalhousie 1921).

Throughout her life, she was generous with both her time and money in organizations such as the Girl Guides, and contributed substantially to the establishment of Kings County Hardwood Lake Girl Guide Camp. She was active in the Red Cross Association, holding the post of president for some time, and was a major contributor to Acadia University, Dalhousie University, and Branksome Hall, Toronto. Through her generosity, the nursing home at Grand View Manor, Berwick, Kings County, was established.

Lalia enjoyed extensive travel, her books, and her rose garden. She remained a very private person, always sensitive to the needs of others, an individual who possessed and enjoyed a good sense of humour. She died in 1979.

Alice Evelyn Thorne

was a medical graduate in 1924. She was born on October 23, 1890, in Karsdale on the Annapolis Basin, Digby County, one of thirteen children born to Joseph and Lydia Wooster Thorne, a Loyalist family who farmed and operated weirs. The Thorne farm is still in operation today.

After attending a one-room school, Alice went to Acadia University and obtained a teacher's licence before she was accepted into Dalhousie Medical School. In the year she graduated, she was found to be suffering from pulmonary tuberculosis, for which the only treatment in those days was bed rest.

She returned home to Karsdale and stayed there until she had recovered. Once she was well again, she went as an intern to the Tuberculosis Sanatorium in Qu'Appelle, Saskatchewan, but found the Prairie winters so harsh that she moved out to the milder climate of British Columbia and made her home with her sister, Mrs. Herberts.

Alice took an internship in the Vancouver General Hospital, but in the male-dominated hospital there was no accommodation for women doctors, so she boarded in the nurses' residence. When her nephews went to visit her, although they were only little boys, they had to sit with her on the porch outside because males were not allowed to set foot inside the nurses' residence.

Meanwhile, two young men from Digby County had settled in Port Kells, fourteen miles from Vancouver, up the Fraser River in British Columbia. They had set up a lumber mill where they cut ties and tie sets for the Canadian National Railway. They shipped timber to the overseas market and dressed lumber for local buyers, and ran a profitable business, even during the Great Depression years.

One of the men, Norman Wade, was from Karsdale and had been a friend of the Thorne family when Alice was a girl. When he learned two of the Thorne girls were in Vancouver, he called at the Herberts' home and met Alice again. They were married in 1932 and Alice went to live in Port Kells, where she cared for the medical needs of the mill hands who were in a hazardous occupation. She was a pioneer occupational medicine specialist.

The marriage was short-lived. Norman Wade died of a coronary thrombosis in 1937 and Alice was left to carry on the business as manager and as a spare hand in the mill when needed. She helped on the green chains—one of the less strenuous jobs.

David Herberts, one of the nephews who, as a boy, had visited her at the nurses' residence recalled in later life,

> She was the only lady mill operator: she was popular, but strict, always acting and dressing as a lady. She maintained community respect, and she supplied lumber gratis to churches, community halls and other charities.

Her nephews visited her every summer vacation and lived in the bunkhouse with the mill hands, while they worked at the mill. They were expected to do as much, or more, than the other employees. They remember that she kept on hand a barrel of dulse from Karsdale, Nova Scotia, as a treat for them.

They grew up to study medicine and become doctors themselves, impressed and inspired by their Aunt Alice who "helped put them through medical school." Both Dr. Edward David Herberts and Dr. Lewis Herberts specialized in urology and are now retired, living in B.C.

Alice remarried and her second husband, Harold Morrison, was a sawyer in the mill.

At the age of sixty-one, on April 8, 1952, Alice died of cancer of the pancreas and was buried in the Church of England graveyard at Cloverdale. She had no children.

Roberta Bond

was born November 3, 1901, in Newfoundland, a daughter of the manse. She was educated at the Halifax Ladies' College, and Mount Allison Academy, and in 1925 she graduated from Dalhousie, MDCM. She returned to her native province and practised for a short time in Newfoundland outports, travelling from a base at Whitbourne, her uncle's ancestral home.

On August 13, 1926, she married Professor E.W. Nichols and moved to Halifax, where her husband was head of the classics department at Dalhousie University.

They had four children, three boys and a girl, and when Professor Nichols died in 1939, Roberta became the sole support of her young family.

She gave anaesthetics in several Halifax Hospitals and was chief anaesthetist at the Children's Hospital. She also joined the faculty of Dalhousie Medical School, becoming the first woman to be lecturer in anatomy in Canada, and later becoming associate professor of anaesthesiology.

During World War II, she was often called out for emergencies when a naval ship came into harbour with wounded on board, after it had been in action or had picked up survivors from vessels sunk in the North Atlantic. She travelled to work by bicycle—a vehicle she shared with her daughter. One of her sons remembers that even on Christmas or Easter mornings, the children awoke to find themselves alone because their mother had been called out to an emergency at one of the hospitals.

In those days there were few women in medical school, and Roberta Bond Nichols took a great interest in women students. Every September, as the new class arrived, she invited the women to an all-day picnic at her summer home in Jeddore.

Roberta was instrumental in organizing the Nova Scotia Branch of the Federation of Medical Women of Canada (FMWC) in 1943, and her home was always open for meetings of the medical women. She was president of the branch on more than one occasion, and served the FMWC as counsellor. She was on the Maude Abbott Scholarship Loan Committee and was national president in 1958-59.

She wrote a history of all women doctors in Nova Scotia up to the year 1924 for her reading club, and had it published in the *Nova Scotia Medical Bulletin* in 1950. It served as valuable source material for Carlotta Hacker, the author of the FMWC's jubilee book, *The Indomitable Lady Doctors.*

In 1966 she attended the Medical Women's International Association meeting in Rochester, N.Y. After several heart attacks forced her to retire, she lead a virtually sedentary life, so contrary to her nature. She died on October 29, 1966.

Dr Richard Saunders was head of the department of anatomy when Dr. Roberta Bond Nichols died, and he said in tribute to her:

> She did much to further the teaching of gross anatomy and never spared herself in assisting the students.... A woman of outstanding energy, warm sympathies, and friendly personality she played an active part in professional and university affairs. With her death the students and staff have lost a staunch friend.

Her photograph was presented to the department of anatomy library on the thirteenth floor of the Sir Charles Tupper Medical Building and the library was named the Roberta Bond Nichols Memorial Collection. Book plates for use in this library were designed by her daughter-in-law, Mrs. R.H. Nichols. The design is

Bookplate in memory of Dr. Roberta
Bond Nichols.

the pitcher plant, the flower emblem of Newfoundland, Roberta's birthplace.

The Nova Scotia Branch of the FMWC also established a Roberta Bond Nichols Memorial Prize in Anatomy, presented annually to the woman medical student who attains the highest standing at the completion of all anatomy courses. The fund is administered by Dalhousie University Medical Awards Committee, and the prize is pre-sented at a regular meeting of the Nova Scotia Branch of the FMWC.

Recipients of the prize to date are: 1968, Mary Edith Donovan; 1969, Janet Speight; 1970, Avalon Roberts; 1971, Claire Murphy; 1972, Margot McRae; 1973, Heather Sanderson; 1974, Elizabeth Mann; 1975, Minoli Amit; 1976, Anne Marie Drysdale; 1977, Anne Marie Gillis; 1978, Giselle Comeau; 1979, Karen MacLeod; 1980, Lynn Crosby; 1981, Lynn McMorran; 1982, Alison Hilary Brand; 1983, Mai Liis Riives; 1984, Paula Gallant; 1985, Kathleen O'Brien; 1986, Mary Winnifred Mudge O'Connell; 1987, Kimberly Hender; 1988, Sophie Dessureault; 1989, Melanie Lynn MacCara.

Anna Margaret Murray

graduated MDCM in 1925. She was born in Elmfield, Pictou County, May 31, 1895 and attended school in Marshville before going to Sydney Academy where she won the gold medal for excellence. She taught school locally and in western Canada until she enroled at Dalhousie Medical School.

She interned at the Halifax Children's Hospital in 1925 and went to Worcester, Massachusetts, in 1926 and served an internship at Worcester Memorial Hospital. She was the house doctor at the former Belmont Isolation Hospital in Worcester from September 1926 to December 1927, followed by a year in the TB service at Bellevue Hospital, New York City.

In 1929, she moved to Webster, Massachusetts, and spent eight years as assistant to Dr. Leslie Bragg until she engaged in her own private practice. She said in 1958 that she regularly worked a seventy-hour week and had office hours every day but Sunday. She married Arthur H. Klebart of Webster and was a family physician in the town for thirty-six years, retiring in 1963.

The range of her practice was reflected in her membership in several societies: the Massachusetts Medical Society, New England Obstetrical and Gynaecological Society, New England Paediatric Society, Worcester District Medical Society, and the American Academy of Family Physicians. At the 198th anniversary meeting of the Massachusetts Medical Society, Dr. Anna Murray Klebart was presented with a gold badge, having been a society member for fifty years. She died at the age of 86 on July 12, 1981, at the Knollwood Nursing Home in Worcester.

Marion Robertson Irving

was one of three young women who graduated in the class of 1927. She was a daughter of the Irving family of Buctouche, New Brunswick, and a sister of K.C. Irving, who became one of Canada's leading industrialists.

Marion specialized in pathology and worked in this field in Charlottetown and later at the Pathology Institute of the Victoria General Hospital, Halifax.

While in medical school, Marion had fallen in love with a classmate, Harry D. O'Brien, who became a surgeon. Six years after they graduated, they were married on November 14, 1933, in Moncton, New Brunswick. They sailed from Halifax for Montserrat on their honeymoon.

She and her husband lived on Coburg Road, Halifax, and Marion did no more professional work after her marriage. They had one son, John, born in 1938. During World War II, Marion did voluntary war work in Halifax with the Imperial Order Daughters of the Empire and the Navy League Canteen, and Harry served overseas in the Royal Canadian Army Medical Corps. After his return, he was a busy surgeon in the Halifax Infirmary, Camp Hill and Victoria General hospitals. Marion died of heart disease at the age of 51 years on November 19, 1957.

Dr. Marion Irving O'Brien and son, John, c. 1939.

Eva Waddell Mader

graduated from Dalhousie Medical School in 1927. She was born into a medical family on October 7, 1902. Her father was Dr. A. Ivan Mader, a strict authoritarian but a progressive practitioner, and the first doctor in Nova Scotia, perhaps in Canada, to bring in radium for treatment of cancer patients in his airy and spacious private hospital at the corner of Edward Street and Coburg Road, Halifax.

It was in those early years in the private hospital that Eva became an X-ray technician, under the guidance of her autocratic father. The building still stands and is now called Marina Apartments.

The family lived in a spacious red brick house at 59 Morris Street, currently owned by the Technical University of Nova Scotia. For several years, in the 1920s, she lived in the Mader Hospital so that a family member could be "on the spot" after her father's hospital superintendent died in the Spanish influenza epidemic. She gained practical experience in the hospital wards and in the operating room, where she worked as a scrub nurse, and on the day prior to her graduation in 1927, she was the O.R. assistant to her father at an appendectomy.

Apart from the family influence, several external factors decided young Eva Mader in her idealistic choice of a career. As a schoolgirl, she was acquainted with a family living on Young Avenue and, fifty years later, she recalled the deep effect on her when one after the other, five brothers and sisters died of diphtheria—one of the terrible childhood scourges of those days.

"After working at the Halifax Dispensary, I got the idea of being a super-preventive specialist," she said.

In the first years of her medical career in Ontario, she was able to give combat to the decimating disease. One of the most far-reaching and satisfying health programs she embarked on personally was the immunization of five thousand children each year between 1929 and 1934. Within five years, she said, there were no cases of diphtheria in Toronto. There had been 500 during her first year in the city.

Eva Waddell Mader was educated at Halifax Academy and Acadia Seminary before entering Dalhousie Medical School. In 1926, she was ready to enter the Halifax Children's Hospital for a year's internship when her mother died. Her father expected her to give up her internship and keep house for him, but she refused. She completed her internship and graduated MDCM, in 1927, after a seven-year course.

The next year she interned at the Nova Scotia Sanatorium and then she joined the University of Toronto School of Hygiene where she obtained a Diploma of Public Health. In 1929 she began her long association with Women's College Hospital, and in 1931 she was married to Charles Norman Macdonald, an insurance businessman, and they had two sons, Fraser and James.

She continued her work as staff physician, bacteriologist and director of laboratories from 1947 to 1952, was chief of the outpatient department and director of the hospital's health services from 1952 to 1956.

During the war years she grew penicillin for the Canadian Armed Forces in whisky bottles, ran a school for technicians and operated a blood bank. She was also a pioneer of rhesus factor tests for pregnant women. In 1952 she entered private practice and continued as a family physician for ten years.

Dr. Eva Mader Macdonald took part in many activities and received many honors: she was certified in bacteriology by the Royal College of Physicians and Surgeons of Canada; holds senior membership in the Canadian Medical Association; honorary life membership in the Federation of Medical Women of Canada, of which she is a past-president, and she was the driving force behind the writing of the book *The Indomitable Lady Doctors.*

In 1973, at age seventy-two, she was installed as Chancellor of the University of Toronto, and a few months later she was named Alumnus of the Year, Dalhousie Medical Alumni Association.

She has been active in the Canadian Red Cross, The Children's Aid Society, The Family Planning Association, University Women's Club, Canadian Welfare Council, Young Women's Christian Association and the alumni associations of Dalhousie and Toronto universities.

During her student years, she was a member of the basketball team and the debating team. She was the badminton champion of Nova Scotia and played tennis and golf.

Today, Dr. Eva Mader Macdonald is very active and says she has something to go to and do every day.

> I have always been busy, doing the best I can in whatever field needed me at the time. It has all paid off. I am having a wonderful old age.

Evelyn Frances Hyslop Rogers

was one of three women in the class of 1927, although she joined the class in the medical school a year after the other students.

She was a daughter of Allan and Beatrice (Hyslop) Rogers, born on February 17, 1904 in Springhill, Nova Scotia. Her father died while Evelyn was a young girl and she moved with the family to Halifax and lived in an apartment near the Willow Tree with her sister, Gertrude, and their mother, who was crippled with arthritis.

Mrs. Rogers had a wealthy brother in the United States and after graduation, Evelyn went to New York, where she interned for a year at St. Luke's Roosevelt Hospital Center, and for a year at Englewood Hospital in Englewood, New Jersey.

In the summer of 1928, her classmate, Eva Mader, wrote to her from the Nova Scotia Sanatorium, where she was an intern. Dalhousie women graduates sometimes referred to themselves as "externs" because so many local hospitals, for example, the Victoria General Hospital, Halifax, declined to have female interns.

Dr. Mader had been offered a fellowship which would take her to Toronto, but she could not accept it unless she found somebody to take her place at the sanatorium. Evelyn agreed to return to

Nova Scotia. She took over Eva's internship and she stayed at the Nova Scotia Sanatorium from September 1928 until March 1930. In 1931 she was at Willard Parker Hospital in New York and at Sea View Hospital at Staten Island, N.Y.

Dr. Rogers' specialty was public health and she received her Diploma of Public Health at Johns Hopkins University. She had a successful career, eventually becoming the medical officer of health for one quarter of New York State. She never married but according to her lifelong friend and classmate, Dr. Eva Mader Macdonald, she had plenty of men friends—"some very special ones." Dr. Evelyn Rogers died in Utica, New York, on May 13, 1987.

Charlotte Munn,

born in Marshfield, August 16, 1902, was the only woman in the class of 1928. Immediately after graduation, she left for the United States, and from May 1928 until July 1932 she was a resident at the Manhattan Psychiatric Center, New York. Following this, she practised psychiatry, and was a member of the American Psychiatric Association. She married William O'Neil. She was associated with the Rockland State Hospital in Orangeburg, New York. She died March 21, 1980.

Irene Viola Allen

was in the class of 1929. She was born in 1904 and graduated from Dalhousie University, receiving her BA in 1925 and her MDCM in 1929.

Later, she recalled her undergraduate years in this way:

> In the summers from 1922 to 1928, I lived at home in Summerside, where I helped my mother in household duties. I played tennis, went swimming, hiking and on fishing trips with my father. I also visited in the nearby country at the homes of my father's sisters, one of whom had a farm, and the other operated a lobster factory and hired the fishing crew.
>
> What a delight to dangle my feet over the cliff and with the tide high, and a wind blowing, to feel the spray, as I watched the lobster boats returning with their catch!

As an undergraduate in her semi-final year, she was a resident intern at the Children's Hospital, Halifax, and the resident intern in the Grace Maternity Hospital in her final year.

Following two years of rotating internship at the Saint John General Hospital, she joined the staff of the Tuberculosis Hospital

Dr. Macpherson with her grandmother, Nanna Brace.

at East Saint John, and was married to classmate Dr. Lachlan Macpherson, a Newfoundlander. She remained working in Saint John until 1960, when she retired because of the health of her husband.

In November 1988, Dr. Irene Allen wrote, "We both were dedicated to the service of helping suffering humanity and were well pleased with the results of chemotherapy during that time."

She had started to practise medicine in the years when bed rest was the only therapy offered patients with tuberculosis, and she had known great joy when the treatment of TB was revolutionized by the development of anti-tuberculosis drugs. They offered recovery and hope.

Dr. Allen recalled one patient in particular in that era—a girl under ten years of age, admitted unconscious with tuberculous meningitis, who recovered with the new drug therapy. She and her husband helped to celebrate the girl's graduation from high school in northeast New Brunswick, and later learned she had kept well, had married and had given birth to a healthy child.

> The years following the discovery of streptomycin were glorious years, seeing patients recover from previously fatal tuberculosis. My one hundred percent service to suffering humanity gave me great satisfaction.

My desire has been for many years to leave this good earth better for my being here, hence, my support of environmental groups, the Ploughshares, and my opposition to nuclear weapons production.

Her husband, Lachlan, died in 1985, having had flares of the tuberculosis he had contracted in his pre-medical days. Dr. Allen wrote that his name and his goodness would live on as long as there were patients who remembered him and how he had touched their lives.

Since 1975, Dr. Allen has lived at 20 Prince Edward Street, Saint John. She is almost blind and uses a white cane when out of doors. She has a housekeeper who is employed five days a week to look after her needs. Only five feet one inch tall and weighing ninety-five pounds, she keeps fit, rising early and swimming each day between 7 and 7.30 a.m. She enjoys listening to classical music and she still corresponds by using a black felt pen on white paper when writing—the easier to see with dimmed eyes—and at age 85, she writes that she lives "with inner serenity," and enjoys life, "here and now."

Dr. Irene Allen, BA, MDCM, LMCC, FCCP, FACP, is a life member of the New Brunswick Medical Society.

Anna Isabel Murray

was born in Earltown, Colchester County, and was in the class of 1929. Her sister was the famed medical missionary, Dr. Florence Murray, who had graduated ten years before.

After graduation, Anna worked for a year as assistant to Dr. Judson V. Graham in Halifax, and in 1930, she was married to George D. Dike, a graduate of the University of Kings College and the Nova Scotia Technical College (now the Technical University of Nova Scotia). They met through a social given for university students at St. Matthew's Church.

They moved to Ontario, where he worked as an engineer with Bell Telephone Company in Toronto. She opened an office and joined the outpatient and inpatient staff of the Women's College Hospital. She ran a medical clinic at a mission from 1930 to 1940, a blood clinic on two mornings a week from 1940 to 1945, and medical, skin and special clinics at Women's College Hospital from 1930 to 1964, when she and her husband retired to Clarksburg, Ontario.

Her husband died in 1970, and in 1981, she married Arthur H. K. Musgrave and they too live in Clarksburg.

In September 1988, Anna wrote "Art and I (Art is 94) are still able to live in our own house and avoid the horrors of a nursing home. Neither of us should live alone. I can get meals and Art can drive our car."

She wrote her letter by hand and signed it: Anna Murray Dike Musgrave.

Jean Whittier,

who graduated in 1929, grew up on a farm in Rawdon, Nova Scotia. Her mother died when she was fifteen so her father's sister took care of Jean, her older sister, Catherine, and her younger brother, Ralph.

From her earliest years, Jean was accustomed to helping to care for people. Her grandfather was paralysed and bedridden for four years before he died, and three uncles, who were living with them at the farm, all died in one winter.

While Jean was at home, the farm chores were shared by the sisters and brother. She was never aware that certain work should not be undertaken by women. She took correspondence courses in nursing and midwifery, and a course in teaching at Normal School, but she decided to go on and become a doctor.

While her older sister, Catherine, was studying medicine at Toronto, Jean attended Dalhousie, living for the first two years in the newly built Shirreff Hall. She says she was glad of that because she was very shy. Then her father died, which left Jean's aunt free to come to Halifax and keep house for her.

In her second year of medicine at Dalhousie, Jean was joined by Anna Murray and Irene Allen. She wrote in her autobiography *My Life's Tapestry*, that she owed much to Anna, for it was she who recommended she get a physical examination.

Jean followed her advice only to find she had early tuberculosis. She did not give up her studies, but went to class in the mornings, then straight to bed until the next day. Her friends stood by her and helped her, and they all graduated together in 1929. She loved all her fellow students and about the boys, she said, "They were very good to me, perfect to me, if you could say that about boys."

With her health a problem, Jean felt she could not stand the strain of an internship and considered undertaking medical research. But after graduating, she served as medical supervisor and teacher of algebra and geometry at the Maritime Home for Girls, Truro. After spending three years in Truro, she took graduate courses at the Women's College Hospital, Toronto, and the United Church Training School.

Her sister, Catherine, had gone to India as a medical missionary in 1927 and Jean was anxious to join her. She was accepted as a medical missionary, and, in 1934, when Catherine returned after her first furlough, Jean went with her, accompanied by their seventy-seven-year-old aunt.

Following a year of language study, she was appointed to the hospital at Banswara, and embarked on a thirty-two-year career of busy devoted service in India. Most of her work was in the Banswara hospital, but she also served in Neemuch, Ratlam and Indore. By the time she retired, the hospital had grown from a small bungalow to a 120-bed hospital, a dispensary and a training school for nurses.

She stated that at one time, she was chief of surgery, chief of medicine, chief of obstetrics and gynaecology, chief of paediatrics, and head of the tuberculosis wards.

One of her most frequent tasks was to deliver babies, many of which were born by Caesarian section. She taught a midwifery program and the students had to deliver twenty babies and attend five difficult births before graduating. "So I did the abnormals and they did the others," said Jean.

During her first term in India a little baby girl was left at the hospital. She was one of the many abandoned "unwanted" ones in India. Jean adopted her and named her Lalita. Until she was a toddler she was allowed the run of the hospital; then Jean put her with a good family and saw that she was well cared for. In time, Jean sent her to a boarding school and then to teacher training college. When she was married, Jean proudly played the part of "mother of the bride," and Lalita named the first of her three children Jean Shirley.

Jean's hobby was making needlepoint tapestries and she completed many, some of which are in India decorating chapels and churches. In 1966, Dr. Jean Whittier retired and lived in Toronto, spending her summers in Nova Scotia at the house in Rawdon where she was born. She wrote her autobiography, *My Life's Tapestry,* in which are many of her poems and line drawings.

In 1979, Dalhousie University conferred on her an honorary degree, LLD. She moved to The Elms Nursing Home in Windsor in 1983, and the following year, she was named Medical Alumnus of the Year.

Dr. Jean Whittier died at Windsor in April 1987.

Appendix

Women's Medical Organizations

In 1919 one of the oldest international medical associations was organized—The Medical Women's International Association. This association holds steadfastly to the aims it has developed through the years and the group now has more than 16,000 members from 63 countries.

The Association's aims are:

1. To stimulate, encourage and promote the entry of women into the medical and allied sciences throughout the world and assist them in the best use of their medical training; and to search for ways to solve the problems of medical women with small children.

2. To provide opportunities for medical women to meet and discuss problems of mutual interest, particularly where they can make a unique contribution as women and as physicians to the community.

3. To foster friendship and understanding among medical women throughout the world without regard to race, religion or political views; affiliation is open to all medical women licensed to practice in their country;

4. To overcome any remaining discrimination between men and women physicians concerning remuneration and pursuit of their careers.

The purposes are to aid medical women, particularly in the developing countries, to obtain fellowships or scholarships for study abroad, and grants for travel to attend scientific assemblies; to provide hospitality to medical women visitors from other countries, and to provide them with information and advice concerning current programmes of medical institutions; to afford medical women the opportunity to work on common problems together and to gain the co-operation of medical women in matters of international health; and to encourage medical women to form national associations where none exist, and where the numbers warrant this.

In 1924, the Federation of Medical Women of Canada was founded at the Glebe Collegiate Institute in Ottawa with seven founding members. It is an independent member of the Medical Women's International Association.

In 1964 the Federation of Medical Women of Canada was given affiliate status by the Canadian Medical Association (CMA), and was granted a seat on the General Council of CMA.

The objectives of the Federation are to promote the interests of medical women in Canada; to aid and encourage pre-medical, medical and post-graduate medical women students; to co-operate with the Canadian Medical Association and the Medical Women's International Association; and to establish and administer scholarship and loan funds.

CRESTS

The crest of the Medical Women's International Association is the figure of Hygieia, the goddess of health and the inscription is: *MATRIS ANIMO CURANT.*

The crest of the Federation of Medical Women of Canada is the staff and snake of Aesculapius with the addition of a single wing, symbolizing the spread of peace through the alleviation of disease and ignorance.

The Nova Scotia Branch of the Federation of Medical Women of Canada was organized in Halifax in 1943 under the leadership of Dr. Roberta Bond Nichols.

The charter members of the Nova Scotia Branch of the Federation of Medical Women of Canada are pictured here. *(left to right, at rear)* Dr. Roberta Bond Nichols and Cdr. Marion Templin; *(front)* Dr. Mabel Patterson, Dr. Ella Hopgood, Dr. Margaret Gosse, Dr. Florence Murray, Dr. Moya Saunders, Dr. Jane Heartz Bell, and Dr. Margaret Corston.

An Historical Note About Dalhousie Medical School

The beginnings of Dalhousie Medical School were troublesome. For some years, doctors in Halifax desired to establish a medical faculty at Dalhousie University, but hesitated due to the lack of a modern teaching hospital and legal approval for dissection. There had been a city hospital located on the site of the current Ambulatory Care Centre, but it had been closed because it was "too expensive to maintain." When Sir Charles Tupper was premier of Nova Scotia, he supported those who wanted a medical school and he introduced the Anatomy Act of 1868. That same year, the city hospital was opened and the medical school was established at Dalhousie, and by 1872 four doctors had graduated.

In 1873, Dalhousie had to close the medical school due to lack of finances. The faculty members, who offered their time gratis, managed to obtain a government grant of $800 a year and they established the Halifax Medical College at the corner of College and Carleton streets in 1875. In that same year, a dispute over the appointment of a certain new graduate as resident house-surgeon caused the Halifax Medical College to close and the doctors to demand "no interference with Medicine by Government or Hospital Boards." The provincial government then took over the hospital and in 1887 renamed it the Victoria General Hospital, in which year, the Halifax Medical College was opened again.

In 1910, the Flexner survey of Canadian hospitals made an uncomplimentary report about the Halifax Medical College and there followed a complete re-organization resulting in full-time clinical teachers and strict entrance requirements. In 1911, the medical school became a Faculty of Medicine at Dalhousie University, which it has been ever since.

In this book, we have referred to Dalhousie Medical School, even though those women who attended between the years 1890 and 1911 were actually attending the Halifax Medical College affiliated with Dalhousie University.

Chester B. Stewart, Former Dean of Medicine, Published in the Halifax Mail Star, September 14, 1968.

SOURCES.

Annie Hamilton: *Macleans*, 1915; letters to Mrs. Ada Spidle, 1931; letter to "Carrie," 1931; letter to Benjamin Hamilton, 1931; Nova Scotia Medical Bulletin, 1950, Roberta Nichols; *The Indomitable Lady Doctors*, 1974, Carlotta Hacker; Colchester Women, 1978, Colchester Historical Society; Knox Church, Brookfield.

Katherine MacKay: *Macleans*, May 1915; *N.S. Medical Bulletin*, 1925, obituary; The Scotsburn Congregation, Pictou Co., Its History, 1925, by Rev. John Murray, DD.; *N.S. Medical Bulletin*, 1950, Nichols; *The Indomitable Lady Doctors*, 1974, Hacker; personal correspondence.

Clara Olding: Grandson, Gordon Hebb; Halifax *Herald*, obituary; *N.S. Medical Bulletin*, obituary; *N.S. Medical Bulletin*, 1950, Nichols.

Martha Shaw: *N.S. Medical Bulletin*, 27:116, obituary.

Leila Randall: *N.S. Medical Bulletin*, 1950, Nichols; personal correspondence with Paul Randall.

Winnifred Braine: *N.S. Medical Bulletin*, 1950, Nichols; CMAJ, 1942, 47:491.

Victoria Ernst: *N.S. Medical Bulletin*, 19:558, 1940; *The Indomitable Lady Doctors*, 1974, Hacker.

Florence O'Donnell: personal correspondence with son, Rear-Admiral Desmond Piers.

Martha Philp: United Church of Canada (UCC) Archives.

Minna May Austen: UCC Archives, Canadian Deaconesses; *The Indomitable Lady Doctors*, 1974, Hacker; CMAJ 1923. p. 542; *N.S. Medical Bulletin*, Dec. 1923, obituary.

Grace Rice: *Macleans*, May, 1915; *N.S. Medical Bulletin*, 1950, Nicols; *The Indomitable Lady Doctors*, 1974, Hacker; personal correspondence with Audrey Murray.

Eliza MacKenzie: *N.S. Medical Bulletin*, 1950, Nichols.

Jemima MacKenzie: Pictou *Advocate*, 22 July, 1981; Dayspring Service Pictou Presbyteries, 2 Aug, 1981; UCC Biographical files; The United Churchman, 7 Feb, 1957; UCC Maritime Conference Archives; *N.S. Medical Bulletin*, 1950 Nichols; personal correspondence.

Stella Messenger: *N.S. Medical Bulletin*, 1933, obituary; *N.S. Medical Bulletin*, 1950, Nichols.

Blanche Munro: *Macleans*, May, 1915; *N.S. Medical Bulletin*, 1950, Nichols.

Mary MacKenzie: *N.S. Medical Bulletin*, 1955, Currie; personal correspondence with Mina E. Patterson.

Annie Hennigar: *N.S. Medical Bulletin*, 1950, Nichols; personal correspondence.

Bessie Bober: *N.S. Medical Bulletin*, 1950, Nichols.

Minnie Spencer: *N.S. Medical Bulletin*, 1950, Nichols.

Eliza Brison: N.S. Dept. of Welfare, 1971, Martha Malsen; *The Indomitable Lady Doctors*, 1974, Hacker.

Bessie Balcom: conversation with son, Paul Davis.

Jean MacLean: conversation with daughter, Ruth.

Elizabeth Kilpatrick: MeDal 1973; c.v. from Dalhousie files.

Louise Pennington: *The Indomitable Lady Doctors*, 1974, Hacker; *N.S. Medical Bulletin*, 1955, Currie.

Florence Murray: autobiography, *At the Foot of Dragon Hill*; In *The Vanguard*, 1976, Lilla Stirling; *N.S. Medical Bulletin*, vols 22 and 25, Murray.; personal letters, 1959, 1964, 1965.

Annie Anderson: correspondence from son, Archibald Dickson.

Ella Hopgood: CMAJ., 76:694, 1957; *The Indomitable Lady Doctors*, 1974, Hacker.

Mabel Patterson: *N.S. Medical Bulletin*, 1955, Currie; personal communication with patients.

Mildred Resnick: personal communication with son, Richard Glube.

Grace Cragg: letters from niece, Margaret, and nephew, Richard.

Anna Creighton: personal communication.

Christine MacLeod: Nephews, Murdoch and Kenneth; personal memories.

Bess Thurrott: correspondence with niece, Mary; MeDal, 1980; Maritime Conference UCC biographical files.

Margaret Chase: correspondence with son, Alan Collins.

Phebe Christianson: personal letters to Dr. Judith Fingard; C.V.; personal communication.

Lalia Chase: correspondence with nephew, Edward Chase.

Alice Thorne: correspondence with nephews, Lewis and David Herberts.

Roberta Bond: communication with sons, John and Digory.

Anna Murray: c.v. from American Medical Association; Worcester *Telegram*, 14 July, 1981, obituary; correspondence with Helen Rand.

Marion Irving: communication with son, John O'Brien.

Eva Mader: MeDal, 1975, Hinds; In The Vanguard, Lilla Stirling; personal correspondence.

Evelyn Rogers: c.v. from American Medical Association; letters from Eva Mader Macdonald; correspondence with cousin, Betty Hall.

Charlotte Munn: c.v. from American Medical Association.

Irene Allen: personal correspondence; letter to Dr. Judith Fingard.

Anna Isabel Murray: personal correspondence; letter to Dr. Judith Fingard.

Jean Whittier: MeDal, 1984; *The Vanguard*, Stirling; *N.S. Medical Bulletin*, 1979; Autobiography, *My Life's Tapestry*.